My dear Henslow. —

I have just returned from London
had the Cordilleras by two passes. This
added much to my knowledge of the
the country. Some of the facts, of which
own mind feel fully convinced, will appear
be absurd & incredible. — I will give
a sketch of the structure of these huge
the Portillo pass (the more Southern one) have
cross) the Cordilleras to consist of a double
near equal altitude, separated by a conside-
terval. — This is the case; & the same thing
ads to the Northward to Uspallata; the latter
the Eastern line; done it more than 6000-7
used it almost to be overlooked. To begin
tem & principal chain; we have where the deel
t seen, an enormous mass of a Porphyritic c
ting on granite. This latter rock, seems to
nucleus of the whole mass & is seen in the
tied valleys, injected amongst eyfleaing, overturnia
most extending manner the overlying strata.
the sides of the mountains, the complicated

DARWIN AND HENSLOW
The Growth of an Idea

Darwin and Henslow

THE GROWTH OF AN IDEA

Letters 1831–1860 edited by

NORA BARLOW

for the Bentham–Moxon Trust

UNIVERSITY OF CALIFORNIA PRESS

Berkeley and Los Angeles · 1967

University of California Press
Berkeley and Los Angeles, California

Printed in Great Britain

CONTENTS

Preface   ix

Introduction   1

Fly-leaf of the Kew Volume   23

Abbreviations used   24

Part I: Letters 1831–7   25

Part II: Letters 1838–60   147

Bibliography   217

Appendices
    I Darwin's recollections of J. S. Henslow   221
    II Darwin's publications   227
    III Darwin's advice to collectors   230
    IV Darwin and coral islands, by D. R. Stoddart   234
    V List of Letters   236
    VI Itinerary of the voyage of H.M.S. *Beagle*   241
Index   245

ILLUSTRATIONS

Charles Darwin, 1840. *facing* 52

Captain Robert FitzRoy, Commander of H.M.S.
Beagle, c. 1836. 53
>From a drawing in the possession of Miss Eileen Smyth,
Dymock, Glos., by her kind permission.

'Fuegian wigwams at Hope Harbour in the Magdalen
Channel.' 68
>From *Voyages of the Beagle* (1839), vol. I, p. 126. P. P.
King.

Fuegian natives in the Straits of Magellan, nearly one
hundred years after Darwin's visit. 69

'Fuegians going to trade their children as slaves with
the Patagonians.' 132
>From *Voyages of the Beagle* (1839), vol. II, p. 171. R. FitzRoy.

'Breast ploughing at Chiloe.' 133
>From *Voyages of the Beagle* (1839), vol. I, p. 287. P. P. King.

John Stevens Henslow, F.L.S., by T. H. Maguire,
1849. (From *Ipswich Museum Portraits*, published
c. 1850.) 148
Reproduced by permission of the Syndics of the Fitzwilliam
Museum, Cambridge.

Charles Robert Darwin, F.R.S., by T. H. Maguire,
1849. (From *Ipswich Museum Portraits*.) 149
Reproduced by permission of the Syndics of the Fitzwilliam
Museum, Cambridge.

FIGURE
Contemporary diagram of H.M.S. *Beagle*.   *page* 48
    By kind permission of Sir Geoffrey Keynes.

MAPS   *fold-out facing page* 236
'Southern portion of South America. Eight Principal Inland
Expeditions.'

'General Chart shewing the Principal Tracks of H.M.S.
Beagle, 1831–6.'
    Both reproduced from *Journal of Researches* (1839). *See*
    Bibliography, p. 218.

PREFACE

The originals of the one hundred and twenty-one letters included in this volume are with three exceptions either in the Library of the Royal Botanic Gardens, Kew, or in the Cambridge University Library. Both Sir George Taylor, Director of Kew Gardens, who first suggested that I should publish the Kew material, and Mr H. R. Creswick, Librarian of Cambridge University Library, have given me every facility. For their help I am most grateful. The first exception to the two main sources is Letter 66, taken from a copy of a letter brought back to me from the United States by Dr Sydney Smith; the second, Letter 78, was kindly sent me by the Librarian of the American Philosophical Society, Philadelphia; the third, Letter 113, is taken from Leonard Huxley's *Life and Letters of Sir J. D. Hooker*, with kind permission of Sir John Murray.

The source of each letter where known is given in the List of Letters, p. 236; together with a statement as to whether it has been previously published.

I am very much indebted to D. R. Stoddart, whose recent researches on Coral Islands, given in Appendix IV, p. 234, brings our knowledge up to date. (*See also* Letter 48.)

Dr F. W. Dunning of the Geological Survey and Museum has given me an informative note on Darwin's observations on the Saint Peter and Saint Paul's Rocks in the light of recent knowledge, for which I am most grateful. (*See* Letter 19.)

I should also like to record my deep indebtedness to the late Mr Noel Y. Sandwith of the Kew Herbarium, who supplied me with the valuable and learned footnotes on botanical matters, written shortly before his most untimely death. These footnotes bear the initials N.Y.S. (*See* Letters 31, 33, 34, 38, 41, 44, 46, 48, 50, 51, 79, 85, 99.)

Mr P. J. Gautrey gave me constant help while I was working in the Anderson Room of the Cambridge University Library, where his knowledge of the Darwin material was of great service.

To those who have given me encouragement in many forms I am most grateful. Miss Sybil Fountain's appreciation of the letters themselves and her discriminating criticism, and Miss Joyce Taylor's orderly mind, have supported me through many delays. Dr Sydney Smith, with his great knowledge of Charles Darwin's annotated books and the Darwin MSS. in the Cambridge University Library, has come to my aid on many occasions.

Lastly I cannot thank Mrs K. West enough, whose critical sense of values, at a late stage in the negotiations with my publisher, helped to bring this work to a conclusion.

Part I: Letters 1–56, 1831–7

The early letters tell the story of how Charles Darwin came to receive the offer of the place of naturalist on board the surveying vessel H.M.S. *Beagle*, and how he nearly refused it. The main narrative of the voyage is told in the series of letters now preserved in the Kew Library. Added chronologically are seven letters from Henslow to Darwin, of which four were included at a late stage in my preparation of the script when Professor Loewenberg drew my attention to their importance. These letters, numbers 14, 17, 22 and 28, form part of a recent acquisition of Darwin material to Cambridge University Library. Amongst other late acquisitions, Mr Gautrey found a sheaf of copies of letters from Darwin to Henslow, from which I have included numbers 65 and 70. These copies were probably used by Francis Darwin in preparing *Life and Letters* and *More Letters* for the press; I have not seen the originals. Letter 25, added to my collection at the suggestion of Dr Sydney Smith, is one of the letters from Charles's father Robert, written in his own hand, which may modify the opinion of some of his harsher critics.

The Kew letters are bound in a rigid leather binding dating back more than a hundred years, the tightly-folded sheets adding to the difficulty of the photographer. The volume is prefaced by a hand-written fly-leaf (which is set out on p. 23). Dr Sydney Smith's suggestion that both the preface and the binding are the work of William Dawson Turner, 1775–1858 (keen collector and antiquary, and father-in-law to William J. Hooker, Director of Kew Gardens from 1841 to 1865), was confirmed by Mr A. N. L. Munby, Librarian of King's College, Cambridge. He is familiar with William Dawson Turner's handwriting, and told me in addition that Dawson Turner amassed 'all kinds of manuscript collections from members of his family and friends and had them bound. Many of them contained similar notes on their fly-leaves.' These letters from Darwin to Henslow probably became known to Dawson Turner through Henslow's friend William Hooker, long before the closer ties of family and friendship which were to follow; for William Hooker's son Joseph married Henslow's daughter Frances in 1851, and Joseph Hooker became Charles Darwin's closest friend for the last forty years of his life.

Part II: Letters 57–121, 1838–60

The originals (or copies) are in the Cambridge University Library, with the exceptions already mentioned, numbers 66, 78, and 113.

Prior Publications

Extracts from some of these letters have been accessible to readers in *Life and Letters of Charles Darwin* edited by Francis Darwin, whilst further selections were included in *More Letters*, edited by Francis Darwin and A. C. Seward in 1903.

Henslow himself, impressed by the scientific contents of the letters, gave the Cambridge scientists a foretaste of Darwin's observations; he read extracts at a meeting of the Cambridge Philosophical Society in November 1835, and had these extracts printed in the form of a pamphlet in December, before Darwin's return. Yet with this early vision of Darwin's powers, Henslow's caution made him add the following warning: 'The opinions here expressed must be viewed in no other light than as the first thoughts that occur to a traveller respecting what he sees, before he has had time to collate his Notes, and examine his Collections, with the attention necessary for scientific accuracy.'

When Darwin heard from his sister Catherine of Henslow's action in printing extracts from his letters, he echoed Henslow's scientific caution, and wrote from the Cape of Good Hope in June 1836: 'I have been a good deal horrified by a sentence in your letter where you talk of "the little book with the extracts from your letters". I can only suppose they refer to a few geological details. But I have always written to Henslow in the same careless manner as to you, & to print what has been written without care or accuracy is indeed playing with edged tools.'[1]

Today Darwin's dated first impressions have gained an increasing importance in building up the structure of his thought. In the present volume I have acted in the belief that the sharp and cutting edges of these tools must be historically valuable, and can be best appreciated by as exact a transcript of the letters as I could attain. In the letters used by Henslow for the pamphlet, he made corrections, underlinings and 'improvements' whilst preparing the letters for the press, sometimes difficult to distinguish from Darwin's own alterations. To the best of my powers I have reproduced their original form.

The rare pamphlet of 1835 was reprinted in exact reproduction in 1960 by the Cambridge Philosophical Society, with a Preface by Dr Sydney Smith.

Spelling and Punctuation

Darwin's spelling has been followed. Idiosyncrasies in the early MSS. can help to date doubtful passages, for certain mistakes began to be corrected in 1836. I have sometimes modified punctuation for the ease of the reader. Square brackets contain my notes or additions, in italics; round brackets are Darwin's own.

N.B.

[1] In the *Entomological Magazine*, 1836, 3, pp. 457–60, a few extracts were also printed, for private distribution.

INTRODUCTION

Charles Darwin spent his childhood and schooldays in Shrewsbury, where his father, Dr Robert Darwin (1766–1848), had won a reputation reaching far beyond the borders of Shropshire for his shrewd medical diagnoses. In 1796 Robert married Susannah, daughter of Josiah Wedgwood the potter (1730–95), and at the turn of the century had built a solid red-brick house for himself and his growing family, overlooking the reaches of the Severn. There Charles was born in 1809, the fifth of six children. After their mother's death, when Charles was eight, the elder sisters took charge of the housekeeping for their widowed father, and also of the education of the two younger children. For Charles, however, this régime lasted only a year, for at the age of nine he entered Dr Butler's famous school in the town as a boarder.

His father, hoping that Charles would be a doctor like himself, chose Edinburgh University for his medical training. The elder brother Erasmus had preceded him there; and Charles joined him, dutifully prepared to follow in the family medical tradition. However, his hospital experiences and the medical curriculum soon turned him irrevocably against the doctor's profession; although he none the less made opportunities—as was his way through life—to satisfy his intellectual curiosity and develop his skills. He joined the Plinian Society of Edinburgh, and communicated two small marine discoveries that he had made. But he could not foresee where his passion for natural history would lead him: in the 1830s there were no obvious professional openings for his particular talents. So, with his father's approval, he left Edinburgh and was admitted to Christ's College, Cambridge, on October 15, 1827, with the intention of gaining a degree and ultimately taking Holy Orders.

Such in bare outline was the course of Charles Darwin's life before he first met the Reverend Professor John Stevens Henslow (1796–1861): a meeting of far-reaching consequences. For in 1831 Henslow recommended him for the position of naturalist on board H.M.S. *Beagle* in her circumnavigation of the world under Captain Robert FitzRoy, R.N.

A vivid memory of The Mount, Charles's Shrewsbury home, formed a constant background to the shifting scenes of his five years of travel, and indeed for the remainder of his life. His sisters, to whom he was devoted, formed part of this background memory; though his affection for Caroline was not without some criticism of her efforts to improve him, when—devotedly, but with an elder sister's over-anxiety—she had taken over his education. He remembered to the end of his life how, before entering a room where she was, he would think: 'What will she blame me for next?'

His father's deeply respected figure dominated these boyhood memories. Dr Robert was a prolific talker, finding time in the midst of his busy practice to rule his family by means of two-hour monologues. But he was a good listener, too, at any rate in his medical capacity; for he could help his women patients, when they were mentally disturbed, by drawing out their confidences— thereby showing, before his time, a recognition of the mind's influence over the body. He was, however, quite unable to express himself on paper, and once wrote to Charles: 'You know I never write anything besides answering questions about medicine.'[1] He was so strongly opposed to Professor Henslow's first suggestion that Charles should join the surveying voyage of H.M.S. *Beagle* as naturalist, that he took the trouble to state his objections at considerable length verbally, as will be seen in the enclosure to the letter Charles wrote to him on this occasion (Letter 6, p. 34).

The timing of the *Beagle* offer was dramatic. Charles had got his degree, and was free from the trammels of further examinations. He and his friends had been fired by reading Humboldt's *Personal Narrative*, and were considering a visit to the Canary Islands on their own account. This project, together with the experiences of a geological field-excursion with Professor Sedgwick, forms the subject-matter of the opening letter—a prologue to what was to come.

Today, with our power of hindsight, it is easy to blame Robert

[1] But see Letter 25.

himself was formulating, must have seemed like an enlightenment. One can, for instance, imagine Darwin reading Henslow's paper 'On the examination of a Hybrid Digitalis', or hearing of his interest in monstrosities, or in the species-question in primulas, and how he would at once have found a kindred spirit and an inspiration in the Professor of Botany.

So it followed naturally that by 1831, when these letters begin, Darwin had already become a frequent visitor at Henslow's friendly home in Cambridge, where he and his wife kept open house once a week to all those who shared his keen interest in natural science. Darwin soon felt at ease in this congenial atmosphere; and thus a friendship began that led to far more than the offer of the place of naturalist on board H.M.S. *Beagle*. Between these two men there arose that immeasurable mutual influence that can arise between two unlike but sincere personalities. Darwin—sensitive, inexperienced, anxious—leant heavily on Henslow's wise, perceptive humanity. Henslow, for his part, must have discerned some unusual quality in this fervent young entomologist. He soon helped Darwin, by his talk and shared interests, to attain that faith in his aims and in himself, which his boyhood at Shrewsbury had failed to provide. The discovery of a fellow-enthusiast, in this formal academic atmosphere, brought to Darwin a new sense of purpose in his work.

The letters that follow give, for the first time, a full documentation of how the contact of their two minds helped Darwin, after he left Cambridge in 1830, to meet the challenge of freedom with a new confidence. The deep respect of the first letters was soon warmed by an affectionate sympathy; and this lasted long after those days when Henslow and Darwin were often to be seen together, walking the Cambridge countryside, and perhaps discussing (amongst a host of subjects) the growing rifts in geological orthodoxy. Darwin, in his last years at Cambridge, was distinguished as 'the man who walks with Henslow'. Now, with the change of emphasis, Henslow may be known as 'the man to whom Darwin wrote'. In his *Autobiography* Darwin recorded that his friendship with Henslow was 'a circumstance which influenced my whole career more than any other'. These letters bear out the truth of his judgement, disclosing how their intimacy guided the direction of Darwin's early life.

When Charles left England in the last days of 1831, he could claim little more than the rank of amateur geologist and naturalist: he returned in five years, a scientist who could command the attention of the great men of the day. In the early letters to Henslow, Darwin laid bare the process of his developing thought as the world-panorama began to unfold. His keen eye for detail never obscured his wider vision; each component part was related in his mind to a vast time and space continuum. The idea of change, already paramount in his earliest geological observations, was later to be extended to his biological collections. His eyes were constantly providing the fodder for his theory-making—supplemented by his geological hammer, and the simple microscope installed in his cabin; while each newly-begotten theory demanded fresh facts as tests of reliability. A perfect feed-back system was in operation.

After Charles's return into the hurly-burly of Cambridge and London, where his work involved him in frequent meetings of scientific societies, his early dependence on Henslow inevitably lessened. At first, with his life-long wish to learn from others, he listened to the forum of those scientists whom he most trusted. He wrote his unpublished sketches for the *Origin* in 1842 and 1844—considerable essays of 47 and 163 pages respectively; but there was no open discussion or sharing of his views at that time. He was dependent on the dictates—and loneliness—of his own scientific judgements, for he had not then become intimate with Hooker or Huxley. Henslow always, and to the end, supported his complete integrity; Darwin on his side shielded Henslow from the more disturbing implications of his theories. But intellectually the two men had begun to drift apart.

The letters fall into two organic groups, following the changing circumstances of Darwin's and Henslow's lives, and this book has been divided accordingly.

Part I centres round the theme of the voyage, although Darwin's first letter in the series was written before he had received the offer to join the *Beagle*. A brief record from the year 1830, before the date of receiving the proposal, up to the actual sailing of H.M.S. *Beagle* on December 27, 1831, is given in Darwin's *Journal* in his own words:[1]

1830   Christmas vacation spent at Cambridge. 1830 continued to collect insects, to hunt, shoot & be *quite* idle. Christmas passed my examination for B.A. degree & kept the two following terms.

1831   During these months lived much with Prof[r] Henslow often dining with him & walking with, became slightly acquainted with several of the learned men in Cambridge, which much quickened the zeal which dinner parties & hunting had not destroyed.

In the Spring paid Mr. Dawes a visit with Ramsay, Kirby & talked over an excursion to Teneriffe. In the Spring Henslow persuaded me to think of Geology & introduced me to Sedgwick.

During Midsummer geologized a little in Shropshire.

August.   Went on Geological tour by Llangollen, Ruthven, Conway, Bangor & Kapel Curig where I left Professor Sedgwick & crossed the mountains to Barmouth. Returned to Shrewsbury at end of August. Refused offer of voyage [*Aug. 30, 1831*].

Sept.   Went to Maer returned with Uncle Jos to Shrewsbury [*Sept. 1, 1831*] thence to Cambridge [*Sept. 2, 1831*] London [*Sept. 5, 1831*].

Sept 11   went with Capt FitzRoy in steamer to Plymouth to see Beagle.

Sep 22[d]   returned to Shrewsbury passing through Cambridge.

Oct. 2[d]   Took leave of my home, staid in London.

Oct. 24th   Reached Plymouth.

[1] *Bulletin of the British Museum (Natural History) Historical Series*, vol. 2, no. 1, 1959. Ed. Sir Gavin de Beer, F.R.S. Henceforth referred to as *Bull. B.M. (N.H.)* etc. See Bibliography, p. 217.

October & November.   These months very miserable.
Dec. 10th   Sailed, but were obliged to put back.
Dec. 21st   Put to sea again & were driven back.
Dec. 27th   Sailed from England on our Circumnavigation.

Darwin's diffidence and a certain mistrust in himself are shown in the early letters of the voyage. In May 1832 he wrote from Rio de Janeiro: 'One great source of perplexity to me is an utter ignorance whether I note the right facts, & whether they are of sufficient importance to interest others'. With his growing purpose and increasing grasp, he soon knew his 'right facts': fact-finding and theory were working in harness. Hypotheses, of which he was never short, led to the search for facts; and fact and emergent theories were under constant re-examination.

As the years passed in the *Beagle's* slow progress up and down the coast of the South American continent during the years 1832 to 1835, whilst Captain FitzRoy was meticulously checking and rechecking the charts of the indented coastlines, channels and islands, Darwin took every opportunity to examine the natural history inland. He was constantly absorbed in adding to his ornithological specimens, besides those in other branches of zoology, and in filling notebook after notebook with descriptive notes of the numbered specimens, which take a sense of direction as the years pass. More exciting and suggestive to him than all else, because of his geological theories and growing concentration on species, were the fossilised bones, shells and silicified trees of the mainland, involving a vastly extended time-span.

If the Galapagos Archipelago is included in the panorama of his experience, the timing and areas that influenced his thought can be seen as threefold, as though the curriculum from which he learnt was planned in three overlapping periods. He approached the problems of the Cape Verde Islands and the South American mainland with the knowledge of his Welsh geological tour with Professor Sedgwick fresh in his mind, and confirmed by close study of the first volume of Lyell's *Principles of Geology*,[1] which

[1] This volume, with 'given me by Capt FR' in Charles Darwin's handwriting, is now in the Cambridge University Library.

he had taken with him on Henslow's advice. He immediately began to formulate theories of land-upheaval and subsidence which were to form the background to the uncompleted picture. The stage was set for the second part of the curriculum—the process of species-differentiation through the geological ages. One of the bridges from the geological to the zoological occurred when he found the huge plates of fossil armadillos, whilst at the same time he was observing their small living counterparts. This was first in 1832 at Punta Alta in Patagonia, when he commented on the rarity of Megatherium finds in his *Diary* on October 8: 'This is particularly interesting as the only specimens in Europe are in the King's collection in Madrid, where, for all purposes of science they are nearly as much hidden as if in their primaeval rock'.[1] In November 1832 he wrote to Henslow: 'Immediately I saw them [i.e. the plates of the fossil Megatherium] I thought they must belong to an enormous Armadillo, living species of which genus are so abundant here'. [Letter 21, p. 61.] He sent home the great Megatherium head in 1833; thus it must have been as early as the years 1832–3 that the impression quickened, not only of the past geological importance of these specimens, but of their connection with their living counterparts, the small armadillos then roaming the Pampas.

The question of species-distribution and the geological eras were clear pointers in the problem of species-formation, and the indications in these letters show that variation and specific differentiation were already his biological signposts. Even botanically, where he reckoned himself to be an ignoramus, he had in mind the variation that might have arisen in alien weeds that had become established in South America. [Letter 30, p. 81.]

From June 1834 to September 1835 FitzRoy was occupied with the charts—verifying and correcting the observations of earlier cartographers off the western shores of South America. During these months Darwin made two inland expeditions from

---

[1] *Diary of the Voyage of the 'Beagle'*, edited from the MS. by Nora Barlow, (Cambridge University Press, 1933), p. 106. Henceforth referred to as *D*. See Abbreviations, p. 24 and Bibliography, p. 218.

Valparaiso, lasting twenty-three and thirty-six days respectively; first crossing the Cordillera to Mendoza, and then riding 420 miles to rejoin the *Beagle* at Copiapò. In these long traverses, the differentiation and distribution of living species became visible to him: the barriers of ocean, sterile plain, or mountain range, were closely observed. The small islands off the south-west coast, with their small mammals, were forewarnings of the demonstration to follow at the end of 1835, in the third part of the curriculum. Then, in the Galapagos Archipelago, the significance of the individual bird and reptile populations—differing in the different islands—forced itself upon him.

He was not wholly prepared for this, the third period's last and startling lesson in geographical isolation; for he did not immediately isolate all the specimens from the individual islands. Luckily, however, some of the collections from different islands had been kept separate, and he had already learnt from local inhabitants that the reptiles originating from the different islands could be distinguished at sight. He saw adaptation everywhere; and in seeing this adaptation as an attribute resulting from a constant potential of variation from within, he reached a hypothetical view of species-formation through geological isolation. The foundations of his life's work were laid in the active work of observing and collecting during the years 1832 to 1835, with the problem of species active in his mind. In the slow sea-passages of the last year, before reaching England in October 1836, the teeming questions on biological change were floating in his mind, as well as the closely related questions of geological sequence. The moulding and cementing idea of Natural Selection which was to follow in 1838, after he had returned to England, changed all preceding evolutionary speculations into a scientific process. The growth of Darwin's ideas under this threefold curriculum can be only partly followed in this correspondence, and it is necessary to go elsewhere for the fuller documentation of his approach to the theory of specific differentiation.[1]

[1] See *Ornithological Notes* in *Bull. B.M. (N.H.)*, Vol. 2, No. 7, ed. N. Barlow, in passages mainly written during the last months of the voyage in 1836; and in the

After the *Beagle's* return to England, Darwin immediately re-joined his family at Shrewsbury and visited the Wedgwoods at Maer. He then hastened to deal with his enormous collection at Cambridge. But his work drew him more and more towards London, and in March 1837 he finally took rooms in Great Marlborough Street, near the home of his brother Erasmus.

Erasmus Alvey Darwin, four years Charles's senior, is frequently mentioned in the early letters, and acted as Charles's unofficial agent in arranging for the transport of books to the ports of call on the voyage. He had taught Charles the elements of chemistry whilst they were boys at Shrewsbury, using their father's garden-shed as their laboratory. Erasmus lacked Charles's energy and innate passion for natural history, though he was a great reader and something of a philosopher: 'Philos' remained Charles's nick-name for him to the end. He never married, and followed no pro-fession. In spite of constant ill-health—possibly tubercular damage to one lung[1]—he nevertheless reached the age of seventy-seven. He was an intimate friend of both Carlyles. His house, 6 Queen Anne Street, London, was a great meeting place for his much-loved Darwin and Wedgwood nephews and nieces. To later generations who never knew him, he remains a most endearing hypochondriac with an individual charm.

Henrietta Darwin (later Mrs Lichfield) mentioned in Letter 104, wrote of him in her *Emma Darwin*,[2] where she takes excep-tion to Carlyle's description of Erasmus in his *Reminiscences*, Vol.II, p.208, as 'this honest Darwin'. Henrietta continues: 'I wish it were possible to give any impression of the charm of our Uncle Ras's character. He was the soul of sincerity, but to speak of him as "this honest Darwin" gives an impression of a kind of open-air

---

Transmutation Notebooks, I, II, III and IV, of 1837–9, after his return to England, *Bull. B.M. (N.H.)*, Vol. 2, Nos. 3, 4, 5, 6 and 7, ed. Sir Gavin de Beer. Also Dr Sydney Smith, 'The Origin of "The Origin"', *Advancement of Science*, No. 64, Brit. Assoc., 1960. Also Dr Sydney Smith in *Impulse*, No. 11, 1959.

[1] This possibility was reported to Margaret Keynes by her uncle, Charles's fourth son, Leonard.

[2] *Emma Darwin. A Century of Family Letters*, Vol. II, p. 146. John Murray, London, 1915.

frankness which was entirely unlike our refined, sensitive, reserved, uncle.' His niece, Julia Wedgwood, wrote after his death that she had heard him described as a 'universal solvent'. She added: 'Where he was, the response came more readily, the flow of thought was quicker.'

In the last letters of Part I, Charles Darwin appears as the returned traveller, sorting his material and writing up his notes. He became seriously unwell at this time, and he confides to Henslow his haunting anxiety lest he should be unable to fulfil his exacting programme of work. There were his collections to dispose of—and at first no one seemed to want them, so pre-occupied were the men of science with their own affairs. But Charles Lyell was immediately helpful, and Henslow never failed him. It was to Henslow that he poured out his doubts about the acceptance of the Secretaryship of the Geological Society; it was Henslow who helped him to procure the £1,000 grant from the Government for the publication of the five quarto volumes of the *Zoology of the 'Beagle'*; and it was Henslow who did urgent proof-reading on his behalf for the first edition of his *Journal of Researches*, which was ready for publication in 1837.

During this time Darwin was, however, free from another form of anxiety that might have weighed on a young man embarking on a career that brought in no salary or remuneration. The early letters tell how his father had already financed him during the voyage, for Robert by this time was a wealthy man. From his success as a doctor, and from clever investments, he had built up a small fortune, in addition to which his marriage to Susannah Wedgwood in 1796 brought him a dowry of £25,000. By 1836, when Charles returned to England, Robert was not only financing his own house at Shrewsbury with three unmarried daughters, but was also supporting his two sons. Later it was Robert who advanced the sum of £2,020 for the purchase of Down House in Kent when Charles and his family moved from London in 1842.[1]

Part II of the letters begins in March 1838, when Darwin was

[1] See *Darwin Revalued* by Sir Arthur Keith. Watts and Co., London, 1955.

still living in his rooms in London. He was now an accepted figure in the scientific circles of the day, and the rush of work continued to increase. The groping uncertainty of the earlier letters has vanished; but that other form of anxiety—whether he could keep pace with these ever-growing demands, especially the demands on his pen—remains. For he always found the writing-up and interpretation of his material an exacting and painful labour. The main direction of his life's work had become clear; but he was tormented by the fear that he could not carry it to a conclusion. With the exhausting and uncongenial burden of writing for publication, he again urgently called on Henslow's help in proofreading. The only touch of impatience ever perceptible is when Henslow's dilatoriness in dealing with the botanical collections was holding up Darwin's main work.

On January 29, 1839, Darwin married his first cousin, Emma Wedgwood, Josiah of Maer's daughter: Henslow's letter to Darwin on the subject of his engagement is here introduced (Letter 58, p. 148). At first, Charles and Emma settled in 114 Gower Street,[1] where their first child was born; in 1842 they moved to Down House in Kent. Here Darwin lived with his growing family for the rest of his life, contending with increasing bouts of undiagnosed illness. Many suggestions have been made as to the cause of Darwin's ill-health, first mentioned in Letters 52 and 54 in this volume. Dr S. Adler of Jerusalem has suggested that he contracted Chagas disease in South America, an illness prevalent in the Argentine, Chile and parts of Brazil where the 'great Black Bug of the Pampas', mentioned by Darwin in the *Voyage of the 'Beagle'*, is the most important vector of *Trypanosoma Cruzi*, the causative agent. Any proof of such infection is now well-nigh impossible; but those interested in Darwin's illness should note Letter 54, written when Darwin was in an acute state of anxiety over his load of work. In this, he tells Henslow of his first visit to Dr Clark, and seeks Henslow's advice. The heart symptoms there described are also mentioned in Darwin's *Autobiography*,[2] as

[1] Damaged by enemy action in 1941, and since demolished.
[2] Ed. Nora Barlow, Collins, 1958, p. 79.

manifesting themselves at a much earlier date, while he was waiting 'very miserable' for the delayed sailing of the *Beagle*.[1]

Down House is only fifteen miles from St Paul's. Even today, with suburbia drawing nearer and nearer, the house and village still seem remote; but in the middle of the last century the nearest train connection was at Orpington, five miles away. Thus a day in London meant for Darwin, both a train journey and a drive in his carriage along the narrow country roads. Nor were such journeys rare occurrences; for during the first years of Darwin's married life his scientific engagements called him frequently to London. He attended and read papers at meetings of the Royal Zoological and Geological Societies, and had been the latter's Secretary from February 1838 to February 1841 (see Letter 54, p. 138).

The house had a large garden; and after 1842 the urge grew on Darwin to test by botanical experiment some of his theories—an urge which renewed the need for frequent communication with Henslow. By now, Henslow too had moved into the country, having in 1837 been presented by the Crown with the valuable but exacting living of Hitcham in Suffolk. It was a country of small, uneducated farmers who disapproved of modern agricultural methods, if they had even heard of them, and who paid starvation wages. The labourers, wretchedly housed, lived in almost worse conditions than farm animals. There was no big landowner or squire to support the new vicar, no local gentry with whom he could discuss his plans for reform. Yet Henslow went ahead with them bravely. While never neglecting his pastoral duties, he concentrated on the education of young and old, and on

---

[1] Some references are here given to the literature that has arisen over the question of Darwin's ill-health, demonstrating the conflicting views of the authors.

Adler, S., *Nature*, 1959, Vol. 184, pp. 1102–3. *B.M.J.*, I, pp. 1249–50, May 1960.
Bowlby, J., *B.M.J.*, Mar. 1965.
Hubble, D., *Lancet*, 1943, i, p. 131; 1953, ii, p. 1351; 1954, i, p. 467.
Kohn, L. A., *Bull. Hist. Med.*, Vol. XXXVII, No. 3, 1963, pp. 239–56.
MacNalty, A. S., *Nursing Mirror*, Dec. 4, 1964.
Stecher, R. M., *Ann. Sci.*, Vol. 17, 1961.
Woodruff, A. W., *B.M.J.*, Mar. 1965.

awakening new aspirations to self-help. He started a village school, incorporating his own system of teaching botany, which was later adopted in many other schools. He parcelled out allotments to each family, in the teeth of opposition from farmers, who believed that work on their own land would suffer. He gradually introduced modern methods of manuring, and of combating disease in crops. As the years went on, he held annual shows of flowers and produce, in which his own exhibits of natural history objects, and what he called his 'lecturets', played a popular and stimulating part.

He trained an enthusiastic band of little girls who were taught to collect seeds and plants for Darwin. He also revolutionised the teaching and appreciation of natural history both in schools, and through the use of lectures and exhibits in the local museums. For the first two years he spent the winter months in Cambridge; but after 1839—though he remained Professor of Botany up to his death in 1861, and lectured regularly—the Rectory at Hitcham was his only residence.

But while the community of country and—especially—botanical interests connects the letters of this second series, it should be remembered that Darwin had more absorbing questions on which he was working at the time. Those who are interested should refer to Appendix 2, p. 227, where the major works published by Darwin between the years 1838 and 1861 are listed. I think it is important to emphasise the very heavy burden of literary work under which he was labouring during the whole period covered by the second series of letters; for this preoccupation, together with his ill-health, helps to explain why Darwin no longer reveals himself so openly to his ageing master. Some of the letters in Part II are trivial; but I have included the whole of the Cambridge collection as showing the pattern of their communication. Darwin had had no hesitation in discussing his geological conjectures freely with Henslow in Part I of these letters, however much they revolutionised existing beliefs. But Darwin's work on the origin of species now led him to the *Descent of Man*, and man's creation was a more sacred doctrine to Christian orthodoxy than were the existence of a world deluge, or the ages of continents.

Although Darwin disclosed so little to Henslow of his growing evolutionary theories at this time, there nevertheless persisted an underlying mutual understanding, including Darwin's knowledge of Henslow's limitations as a theorist. Through the flow of Darwin's correspondence there runs—beneath the scientific tone —an undercurrent of warm feeling that never lessens; but the pupil's longing for approval, so apparent in the earlier letters, makes way for the reserved certainty of the master, together with a care for Henslow's beliefs which must have helped to maintain their lasting mutual trust.

Darwin wrote in his recollections of Henslow after his death: 'He talked on all subjects, including his deep sense of religion, and was entirely open.' Darwin must have realised that the Rector of Hitcham, with his parochial duties, and his self-imposed task of establishing the educational value of natural history for old and young, in town and country, had entered on other spheres of usefulness where Darwin could not follow. In the same way he must have known during the voyage of the *Beagle*, many years earlier, that Henslow could not follow him in 'grinding general laws out of large collections of facts'.[1] He could never discuss 'philosophical botany' with Henslow as he could later with Henslow's son-in-law, J. D. Hooker.[2]

This correspondence, so heavily one-sided, is nevertheless a dual portrait. To most readers, even those well-versed in Darwin and his period, Henslow's character must appear charming but shadowy: he was by nature an anonymous saint. His achievements are lost in the accepted recognition of natural history as an educational and agricultural tool in the mid-nineteenth century. If this book makes him stand out as a living personality, with only nine letters in which he speaks with his own voice, and the rest an echo of his influence conveyed in Darwin's words, one of my objects will have been achieved. Henslow's letters, it should be noted, were written mainly at significant turning-points in Darwin's life. The first, Letter 3, p. 29, throws the golden apple of the voyage

---

[1] See *Autobiography*, ed. Nora Barlow, Collins, 1958, p. 139.
[2] See *Life of Hooker*, by L. Huxley, Vol. I, pp. 488 et seq.

of the *Beagle* into Darwin's lap—an opportunity that Henslow himself had considered accepting; the letters written during the voyage helped Darwin to see that voyage to its conclusion when courage almost failed him. Letter 58 (p. 148) is an expression of wisdom on Darwin's coming marriage; and in Letter 113 (p. 205) from Henslow to his son-in-law, Joseph Hooker, Henslow gives his opinion in May, 1860 of Darwin's honesty amidst the storm of abuse and innuendo aroused by the publication of *On the Origin of the Species*.

Thus Henslow's comments can be heard at critical phases throughout Darwin's life. More unpublished letters will doubtless come to light; and more, already published, could have been given. But there must be a frame to the pattern, a selection of material. There are enough here, I believe, to reinforce the figure of Henslow—mainly realised before as a mirrored portrait in the letters of Darwin, and too often neglected as a foil to the brighter light. Apart from presenting Darwin with the chance of his lifetime, Henslow should be given his due for actively furthering the cause of scientific education and scientific farming in the first half of the nineteenth century, preparing the ground for those changes in biological thinking which followed after his death, and in which Darwin had so large a part. A biography with letters to a dozen or more correspondents may give echoes in many different keys; here, a unity is achieved in the single personal relationship, with only the passing of the years bringing its inevitable changes. Darwin, at first the immature and diffident youth, comes to maturity under Henslow's guidance. Henslow had known and watched Darwin for thirty-four years, and, notwithstanding their differences of opinion, never doubted Darwin's complete integrity of purpose.

Hooker wrote of his father-in-law, J. S. Henslow, after his death, as 'a man who, with strong enough religious convictions of his own, had the biggest charity for every heresy so long as it was conscientiously entertained'. Darwin replied to Hooker: 'I fully believe a better man than Henslow never walked this earth.'

PART I

Letters 1831–7

c

FLY-LEAF OF THE KEW VOLUME

[*The small fly-leaf, 5¼ × 3 inches, introducing the letters in the Kew volume, is by William Dawson Turner, grandfather of Joseph Dalton Hooker; Hooker married Henslow's daughter in 1851, and Hooker succeeded his father as Director of Kew Gardens in 1865. Thus the preservation of this bound volume of letters in the Kew Library can be explained.*]

40 letters from C. Darwin to Prof. Henslow of these
11 written from 11 July 1831 to Dec. 3 1831, before C.D. sailed in the Beagle with Capt. Fitzroy to explore the coast of S. America. –
13 from May 13, 1832, to July 12, 1833 written in S.A. or in the Beagle on the Coast.
2 Janry 1836 & July 1836 from Sydney & St Helena on his way home both highly interesting.
1—Oct. 6, 1836 from his father Dr D's house at Shrewsbury immediately on his return London
13—Oct 1836 – Nov 1836 from London & Cambridge, chiefly
40 about preparg for the press. The letters are all most honourable to C.D. for zeal & acute observation & head & heart – Above all, for his affectionate regard to Prof. H. to whom they are hardly less honourable. Geology & mineralogy are C.D's leadg subjects & on these his views are most extensive & acute & original.

ABBREVIATIONS USED

Bull.B.M.(N.H.)   *Bulletin of the British Museum (Natural History) Historical Series.* See Bibliography, p. 217.

D   *Diary of the Voyage of the 'Beagle',* edited from the MS by Nora Barlow. Cambridge University Press, 1933.

LL   *Life and Letters of Charles Darwin,* edited by his son Francis Darwin. 3 vols., John Murray, London, 1887.

ML   *More Letters of Charles Darwin,* edited by Francis Darwin and A. C. Seward. 2 vols., John Murray, London, 1903.

O   *On the Origin of Species by means of Natural Selection or the preservation of favoured races in the struggle for Life.* John Murray, London, 1859.

Z   *Zoology of the 'Beagle'.* See Bibliography, p. 217.

LETTER 1

[*All letters are from Charles Darwin, unless otherwise stated. Letter 1 was written from Darwin's home in Shrewsbury, after the end of his last term at Cambridge in 1831, before receiving the offer to join H.M.S. 'Beagle' on her circumnavigation of the world. The eagerness over the forthcoming geological tour in Wales with Professor Sedgwick, and the determination to visit the Canary Islands with his friends, both give an indication that his scientific career would have found an outlet even if the timely solution of the 'Beagle' voyage had not so soon reached him.*]

[*To: Revd Prof. Henslow, Cambridge*
Postmark: Shrewsbury, Jy 12 1831]

Shrewsbury 11 July 1831
Monday

My dear Sir

I should have written to you some time ago, only I was determined to wait for the Clinometer, & I am very glad to say I think it will answer admirably: I put all the tables in my bedroom, at every conceivable angle & direction. I will venture to say I have measured them as accurately as any Geologist going could do.— It cost 25s made of wood, but the lid with plate of brass graduated. Cary did not approve of a bar for the [under *del*] plumb; so that I had *heavy* ball instead.—I have been working at so many things: that I have not got on much with Geology: I suspect the first expedition I take, clinometer & hammer in hand, will send me back very little wiser & [a] good deal more puzzled than when I started.—As yet I have only indulged in hypotheses; but they are such powerful ones, that I suppose, if they were put into action but for one day, the world would come to an end.—I have not heard from Prof: Sedgwick,[1] so I am afraid he will not pay the

---

[1] Professor Adam Sedgwick, 1785–1873, Woodwardian Professor of Geology since 1818, was to lead the Welsh geological tour, where the clinometer, or instrument for measuring slopes, was to go into action. This tour was the prologue to Darwin's geological enthusiasm. Later in life, Sedgwick strongly opposed Darwin's evolutionary views. See his letter to Darwin, *Life and Letters of Charles*

seven formations a visit.—I hope & trust you did your best to urge him:—and now for the Canaries.—I wrote to Mr. Ramsay,[1] the little information which I got in town.—But as perhaps he had left Cam. I will rehearse it.—Passage 20£: ships touch & return during the months of June to February.—But not seeing myself the Broker, the two most important questions remain unanswered. viz. whether it means June inclusive & how often they sail.—I will find this out before very long.—I hope you continue to fan your Canary ardor: I read & reread Humboldt,[2] do you do the same, & I am sure nothing will prevent us seeing the great Dragon Tree.[3] Would you tell L. Jenyns[4] that his magnificent

---

Darwin, Vol. II, p. 247; henceforth referred to as *LL*. *More Letters of Charles Darwin* will be referred to as *ML*. See Abbreviations, p. 24, and Bibliography, p. 217.

[1] Marmaduke Ramsay, fifth son of Sir Alexander Ramsay, first baronet of Balmain; admitted pensioner at Jesus College, Feb. 11, 1814; fifteenth Wrangler, 1818; M.A., 1821; Fellow of Jesus College, 1819–31. Died at Perth on July 31, 1831. He made a deep impression on C. D., his junior by about ten years, and was a great friend of Henslow's. He had evidently intended to join the Canary party. It was for this trip that Darwin had acquired his smattering of Spanish, later to serve him in good stead. For Ramsay, see also Letters 2, 3, 5, 19, 28 and 31.

[2] Cf. unpublished letter, (C.U.L.), to Charles Darwin from the Baron von Humboldt from Sans Souci, près Potsdam, Sept. 18 1839. 'Vous me dites, dans votre aimable lettre que, très jeune, ma manière d'étudier et de peindre la nature sous la zone torride avait pu contribuer à exciter en vous l'ardeur et le désir des voyages lointains. D'après l'importance de vos travaux, Monsieur, ce ferait là le plus grand succès que mes faibles travaux auraient pu obtenir. Les ouvrages ne sont bons qu'autant qu'ils font naître de meilleurs.'

[3] Dragon Tree. Humboldt wrote in *Ansichten der Natur*, first edition, 1808, of his visit to Teneriffe in 1799; and describes the colossal tree, *Dracaena draco*, standing in the garden of Dr Franqui, the circumference measuring nearly 48 feet, the measurement taken several feet above the ground.

Mrs Sabine published *Aspects of Nature* in 1849, translated from Humboldt's third edition, prepared when he was in his eightieth year.

Willis's *Dictionary of Flowering Plants and Ferns*, sixth edition, 1931, reports 'The famous dragon-tree of Teneriffe (*D. Draco L.*), blown down in 1868, was 70 ft high and 45 ft in girth and was supposed to be 6,000 years old.'

[4] J. S. Henslow's brother-in-law, and often mentioned in the following letters. Leonard Jenyns, 1800–93, became Vicar of Swaffham Bulbeck, near Cambridge, where Darwin often visited him. Good field naturalist, and author of many works on natural history and papers in scientific journals. He almost accepted the offer of the post on H.M.S. *Beagle* before it was offered to Darwin. Later he moved to Bath and took the name Blomefield. After Henslow's death in 1861, he wrote *Memoir of John Stevens Henslow*, published in 1862.

He undertook the fourth volume on Fishes in the quarto volumes on the

present of Diptera has not been wasted on me. Would you ask him how he manages Diptera when too small for a pin to go through.—I am very anxious to hear how Mrs Henslow is—I am afraid she will wish me at the bottom of the Bay of Biscay, for having been the first to think of the Canaries.—I am going now to trouble you with several questions.—Do you know A. Way's[1] direction. Do you by any chance recollect the name [*the end of the letter is written across the writing on MS. p. 2*] of a fly that Mr. Bird sent through Downes.—And now for a troublesome commission, would you be kind enough to exert your well-known judgement & discretion in choosing for me a Stilton Cheese; fit for eating pretty soon.—Would you have it directed to Shrewsbury & I will pay the man when I come up in October.—Excuse all the trouble I am giving you, & Believe me my dear Sir

Yours ever most sincerely
Chas. Darwin

[*Written across MS. p. 3 he adds:*] Eyton[2] begs to be most kindly remembered to you.—his mind is in a fine tropical glow.

Zoology of the 'Beagle', edited by C. Darwin (1839–43). Henceforth referred to as *Z.* See Abbreviations, p. 24, and Bibliography, p. 218.

[1] Albert Way, 1805–74. Antiquarian, traveller and editor of *Promptorium Parvulorum*.

[2] Thomas Campbell Eyton, 1809–80, twenty-third heir of the Eytons of Eyton; wrote *Rarer Birds of Britain*, and *Catalogue of British Birds*, in 1836 and 1838. Started the *Herd Book of Hereford Cattle* in 1842. Friend and correspondent of C. D., Agassiz, Asa Gray, Wallace and Owen. Opposed C. D.'s views and was chagrined to find that his own observations on pigeons were used to support Darwin's theory of evolution.

LETTER 2

To: J. S. Henslow, 7 Suffolk Street, Pall Mall East
From: G. Peacock[1]]

[*Before 24 August*] 1831

My dear Henslow

Captain Fitz Roy[2] is going out to survey the southern coast of Terra del Fuego, & afterwards to visit many of the South Sea Islands & to return by the Indian Archepelago: the vessel is fitted out expressly for scientific purposes, combined with the surveys: it will furnish therefore a rare opportunity for a naturalist & it would be a great misfortune that it should be lost:

An offer has been made to me to recommend a proper person to go out as a naturalist with this expedition: he will be treated with every consideration: the Captain is a young man of very pleasing manners (a nephew of the Duke of Grafton) of great zeal in his profession & who is very highly spoken of: if Leonard Jenyns could go, what treasures he might bring home with him, as the ship would be placed at his disposal, whenever his enquiries made it necessary & desirable: in the absence of so accomplished a naturalist, is there any person whom you could strongly recommend: he must be such a person as would do credit to our recommendation.

Do think on this subject: it would be a serious loss to the cause of natural science, if this fine opportunity was lost

The ship sails about the end of Sept[r].

---

[1] The Rev. George Peacock of Trinity College, Cambridge, and Lowndean Professor of Astronomy, friend of Captain Francis Beaufort, R.N., Hydrographer to the Royal Navy. As regards his inaccuracy, see Letters 4 and 10.

[2] Captain Robert FitzRoy, 1805–65, commanding H.M.S. *Beagle*. He had been on a previous surveying cruise to S. America under Captain King during the years 1826–30. His surveys were noted for their excellence. Became Governor of New Zealand, the settlers petitioning Parliament for his recall. On his return, the science of meteorology and the lifeboat service owed much to his labours. Darwin wrote to his sister in 1832: 'I should not call him a clever man, yet I feel convinced nothing is too great or too high for him. His ascendency over everybody is quite curious.'

Poor Ramsay! what a loss to us all & particularly to you
Write immediately & tell me what can be done

> Believe me
> My dear Henslow
> Most truly yours
> George Peacock

[*Enclosed with Letter 2*]

> 7 Suffolk Street
> Monday

My dear Henslow,
   I wrote this letter on Saturday but I was too late for the Post:
What a glorious opportunity this would be for forming collections for our museums: Do write to me immediately & take care
that the opportunity is not lost

> Believe me
> My dear Henslow
> Most truly yours
> Geo Peacock

LETTER 3

> To be forwarded or opened
> if absent

[*To: C. Darwin Esq., Shrewsbury
From: The Rev J. S. Henslow*]

> Cambridge 24 Aug. 1831

My dear Darwin,
   Before I enter upon the immediate business of this letter, let us
condole together upon the loss of our inestimable friend poor
Ramsay of whose death you have undoubtedly heard long before
this: I will not now dwell upon this painful subject as I shall hope
to see you shortly fully expecting that you will eagerly catch at
the offer which is likely to be made you of a trip to Terra del

Fuego & home by the East Indies—I have been asked by Peacock who will read & forward this to you from London to recommend him a naturalist as companion to Capt Fitzroy employed by Government to survey the S. extremity of America. I have stated that I consider you to be the best qualified person I know of who is likely to undertake such a situation—I state this not on the supposition of yr. being a *finished* Naturalist, but as amply qualified for collecting, observing, & noting anything new to be noted in Natural History. Peacock has the appointment at his disposal & if he cannot find a man willing to take the office, the opportunity will probably be lost. Capt. F. wants a man (I understand) more as a companion than a mere collector & would not take anyone however good a Naturalist who was not recommended to him likewise as a *gentleman*. Particulars of salary etc I know nothing. The Voyage is to last 2 yrs & if you take plenty of Books with you, anything you please may be done—You will have ample opportunities at command—in short I suppose there never was a finer chance for a man of zeal & spirit. Capt F. is a young man—What I wish you to do is instantly to come to Town & consult with Peacock (at No 7 Suffolk Street Pall Mall East or else at the University Club) & learn further particulars—Don't put on any modest doubts or fears about your disqualifications for I assure you I think you are the very man they are in search of—do conceive yourself to be tapped on the Shoulder by your Bum-Bailiff & affect^e friend

J. S. Henslow

(turn over)

The expedn. is to sail on 25 Sept: (at earliest) so there is no time to be lost

LETTER 4

[*To: C. Darwin*
From: George Peacock]

[*no date*]

My dear Sir,

I received Henslow's letter last night too late to forward it to you by the post, a circumstance which I do not regret, as it has given me an opportunity of seeing Captain Beaufort at the Admiralty (the Hydrographer) & of stating to him the offer which I have to make to you: he entirely approves of it & you may consider the situation as at your absolute disposal: I trust that you will accept it as it is an opportunity which should not be lost & I look forward with great interest to the benefit which our collections of natural history may receive from your labours.

The circumstances are these Captain Fitzroy (a nephew of the Duke of Grafton's) sails at the end of September in a ship to survey in the first instance the S. Coast of Terra del Fuego, afterwards to visit the S. Seas Islands & to return by the Indian Archipelago to England: the expedition is entirely for scientific purposes & the ship will generally wait your leisure for researches in natural history etc: Captain Fitzroy is a public spirited & zealous officer, of delightful manners & greatly beloved by all his brother officers: he went with Captain Beechey[1] & spent 1500 L in bringing over & educating at his own charge 3 natives of Patagonia:[2] he engages at his own expense an artist at 200 a year to go with him: you may be sure therefore of having a very pleasant companion, who, will enter heartily into all your views

The ship sails about the end of September & you must lose no time in making known your acceptance to Captain Beaufort & Admiralty Lords

I have had a good deal of correspondence about this matter [*with Henslow*] who feels in common with myself the greatest

---

[1] A mistake for Captain King, with whom Captain FitzRoy had been on a previous voyage to S. America, 1826–30. See footnore 2, p. 40.

[2] See Letter 26, p. 73.

anxiety that you should go: I hope that no other arrangements are likely to interfere with it

Captain will give you the rendezvous & all requisite information: I should recommend you to come up to London in order to see him & to complete your arrangements

I shall leave London on Monday: perhaps you will have the goodness to write to me at Denton, Darlington, to say that you will go

The Admiralty are not disposed to give a salary, though they will furnish you with an official appointment & every accommodation: if a salary should be required however I am inclined to think that it would be granted

> Believe me
> My dear Sir
> very truly yours
> Geo Peacock

If you are with Sedgwick I hope you will give my kind regards to him.

LETTER 5

[To: The Rev^d. Prof. Henslow, Cambridge
Postmark: Aug 30 1831]

> Tuesday 30th August 1831
> Shrewsbury

My dear Sir.

Mr. Peacock's letter arrived on Saturday, & I received it late yesterday evening.—As far as my own mind is concerned I should I think, *certainly* most gladly have accepted the opportunity which you so kindly have offered me.—But my Father, although he does not decidedly refuse me, gives such strong advice against going.—that I should not be comfortable, if I did not follow it.—My Father's objections are these; the unfitting me to settle down as a clergyman.—my little habit of seafaring.—the *shortness of the time* & [his *del*] the chance of [the *del*] my not suit-

ing Captain Fitzroy.—It is certainly a very serious objection, the
very short time for all my preparations, as not only body but mind
wants making up for such an undertaking.—But if it had not been
for my Father, I would have taken all risks.—

What was the reason, that a Naturalist was not long ago fixed
upon?—I am very much obliged for the trouble you have had
about it—there certainly could not have been a better opportunity.—I shall come up in October to Cambridge, when I long
to have some talk with you.—I will write to Mr. Peacock at
Denton, [(in Durham?) *added*] but his direction is written so
badly, that even with the assistance of the Post Office, I am not
certain about it—would you therefore be so kind, if you know his
or C. Fitzroy's direction, would you send one line to the same
effect.—My trip with Sedgwick, answered most perfectly.—I did
not hear of poor Mr. Ramsay's loss till a few days before your
letter. I have been lucky hitherto in never losing any person for
whom I had any esteem or affection. My Acquaintance, although
very short, was sufficient to give me those feelings in a great
degree.—I can hardly make myself believe he is no more.—He
was the finest character I ever knew.—

Yours most sincerely my dear Sir.

Chas. Darwin

[*across beginning of Letter 5*]
I have written to Mr. Peacock, & I mentioned that I have asked
you to send one line in the chance of his not getting my letter.—I
have also asked him to communicate with Cap. Fitzroy.—Even
if I was to go my Father disliking [*it*] would take away all energy,
& I should want a good stock of that.—Again I must thank you;
it adds a little to the heavy but pleasant load of gratitude which I
owe to you.—

LETTER 6

[Written from Maer in Staffordshire, the home of Darwin's uncle, Josiah Wedgwood, and of his future wife, Emma Wedgwood. Enclosing a letter to Dr Robert Darwin from Josiah Wedgwood]

[To: Dr. Robert Darwin
From: Charles Darwin]

[Maer] August 31st, 1831

My dear Father,

I am afraid I am going to make you again very uncomfortable —but upon consideration I think you will excuse me once again stating my opinions on the offer of the voyage. My excuse and reason is the different way all the Wedgwoods view the subject from what you and my sisters do.

I have given Uncle Jos, what I fervently trust is an accurate and full list of your objections, and he is kind enough to give his opinion on all. The list and his answers will be enclosed, but may I beg of you one favour, it will be doing me the greatest kindness if you will send me a decided answer—Yes or No—; If the latter I should be most ungrateful if I did not implicitly yield to your better judgement and to the kindest indulgence which you have shown me all through my life,—and you may rely upon it I will never mention the subject again; if your answer should be Yes, I will go directly to Henslow and consult deliberately with him and then come to Shrewsbury. The danger appears to me and all the Wedgwoods not great—the expence cannot be serious, and the time I do not think anyhow, would be more thrown away than if I staid at home.—But pray do not consider that I am so bent on going, that I would for one single *moment* hesitate if you thought that after a short period you should continue uncomfortable.—I must again state I cannot think it would unfit me hereafter for a steady life.—I do hope this letter will not give you much uneasiness.—I send it by the car tomorrow morning; if you make up your mind directly will you send me an answer on the following day by the same means. If this letter should not find

sooner.—I put it off yesterday & the day before owing to the Coronation¹ & not seeing Cap. FitzRoy & therefore not having anything particular to communicate.—Today I did not come home till too late for the post, having spent it with Cap Fitz going about the town & ordering things.—By this you will perceive it is all settled; that is to say I cannot possibly conceive any cause happening of sufficient weight to alter my determination.— I have ordered pistols & a rifle, both of which by Fitzroys account I shall have plenty of use for.—These really are nearly the only expensive things I shall want: Fitzroy has an immense stock of instruments & books.—viz takes out 5 Simpisometers,² 3 M Barometers.—in books all travels & many natural history books. —He does not appear to care for any expense as far as regards himself, but is very economical with respect to advice to me.— And now for my plans.—Sunday I go packet to Plymouth stay there a few days: then London: then Cam. where I shall finally settle things, pay bills etc & home to Shrewsbury: Then London again: Plymouth: Terra del Fuego.—The SS Islands are all but certain. I am on the books for victual.—but about my collections. Cap Beaufort said his first impression was, that they ought to be given to British Museum? but I think I convinced [*him*] of the impropriety of this & he finished by saying he thought I should have no difficulty so that I presented them to some public body, as Zoological & Geological etc.—But I do not think the Admiralty would approve of my sending them to a Country collection, let it be ever so good.—& really I doubt myself, whether it is not

¹ Of King William IV. See *LL*, I, p. 207. Letter to Susan Darwin.
² 'Sympiesometer. A form of barometer in which the column of liquid in the tube has above it a body of confined air or other gas (instead of a vacuum as in the mercurial barometer) so that the pressure of the atmosphere acts against the weight of the liquid and the elastic pressure of the gas: a thermometer is attached for correction of the readings according to the expansion or contraction of the gas with changes of temperature.' (*O.E.D.*)
The earliest quotation given is 1817, *Blackwood Mag.*, Vol. I, p. 418:
'Mr Adie has given it the name of sympiesometer (or measure of compression).'
In Fitzroy's account of the voyage in the official *Surveying Voyages of Adventure and Beagle*, Vol. II, 1839, pp. 49, 50, he mentions the use of barometer and sympiesometer for guarding against the sudden onslaught of violent squalls. The sympiesometer readings are given in the Appendix throughout the voyage in the Meteorological Journal.

more for the advancement of Nat. Hist. that new things should be
presented to the largest and most central collection.—But we will
talk of all this & many other things when we meet,—which I
should think would be early the week after next.—Mr. Yarrell[1]
has been quite invaluable to me; so very good natured & such
very good advice: But they all say Cap. King[2] will be of the
greatest use.—The Nor[:] of bottles is greatest puzzle.—Will
you see about a iron net for shells.—Remember me most kindly to
L. Jenyns, & tell him I am to have a parcel to bring for him from
Mr. Yarrell: Would you enquire from him, in what Edinburgh
Journal, there are some papers by Coldstream & Foggo? send an
answer to this question.—I must have a rain-gauge.—I hope
when I return from Plymouth I shall find a letter from you: I
received one today from Prof. Sedgwick, but have not yet had
time to read it.—You can have no idea how busy I am all day
long.—& owing to my confidence in Cap Fitzroy I am as happy
as a king: if you were here to talk to, I should be a good deal
happier.—I hope you will excuse all the trouble I give you, if
you were like Liston in Paul Pry[3] to say you never would do a
good natured thing again, I do not know what I should do.—
Good night my dear Henslow

Yours most sincerely
Chas Darwin

P.S. All FitzRoy said about the letter of Peacock evidently from a
very enthusiastic man, an elegant way of calling it inaccurate.[4]

1 William Yarrell, 1784–1856, naturalist, lived his seventy-two years in the
parish of St James's, London, where he carried on the family business of book-
seller and newspaper agent. Wrote *History of British Fishes*, 1835–6; and *History
of British Birds*, 1839–43. Helped to found the Zoological Society in 1826. Vice-
President of Linnean Society.
2 Captain King commanded H.M.S. *Beagle* on a previous voyage to S.
America, 1826–30, his account forming Vol. I of the *Voyages of Adventure and
Beagle, 1826–36*, edited by Captain FitzRoy in 1839, with Darwin's account of
the voyage of 1832–6 as Vol. III.
3 *Paul Pry*, farce published in 1825, by John Poole, 1786?–1872.
4 This comment on the Rev. G. Peacock's inaccuracy (see also Letter 4) may
explain a remark in Captain Beaufort's letter to Henslow, which Sir Gavin de
Beer quotes as evidence that Charles Darwin and his Cambridge friends were
planning to visit S. America. Beaufort writes; 'My dear Sir, I believe my friend

[*Across the top of p. 1 of this letter is added:*] Cary says your Clinometer is ready and he is working at the Camera obscura—it soon will be ready.—I have just been with Cap King, Fitzroy['*s*] senior officer during last expedition & he has given me much good advice: but I am afraid he must have swept the Coast almost clear: I will write again before I come to Cambridge. Keep Syme on colours in your mind.

LETTER 11

[*To: The Revd. Prof: Henslow Cambridge*
Postmark: C.H 17Se 1831]

17 Spring Gardens
Saturday 17th. Sep. 1831

My dear Sir

I arrived this morning from Plymouth & found your letter with six others on my table.—I mention this, as it will account for my [not *del*] writing to you a very short letter.—I called on your brother, but he was not at home, I heard then that you left London yesterday: How very unfortunate it was my being detained in Plymouth: I should have much enjoyed taking a walk in London town with you.—I am much obliged for your asking me to take up my quarters with you: I will most gratefully accept it in every point but one, viz sleeping at your house.—I shall arrive in the middle of the night by the Mail, & after 2 or 3 days shall start *very early* in the morning to Birmingham: So I cannot think of turning your house upside down for merely one night.—Will you be kind enough to order a bed for me at the Hoops' for

Mr. Peacock of Trin. College Cambe has succeeded in getting a "savant" for you —A Mr. Darwin grandson of the well known philosopher and poet—full of zeal and enterprize and having contemplated a voyage on his own to S. America. Let me know how you like the idea that I may go or recede in time. F. B.' Peacock's inaccuracy may have led him to transform the intended visit to the Canaries into a voyage to S. America when writing to Captain Beaufort. The letter is quoted in a footnote in Sir Gavin de Beer's transcript of Darwin's journals or 'little diaries' in which he briefly recorded the bare outline of his movements and work. Not to be confused with Darwin's *Diary of the Beagle*, nor his *Journal of Researches*. See *Bull. B.M.(N.H.)*, Vol. 2, Nos. 1–6.

Monday night: as it is almost certain I shall come to Cambridge then.—You may tremble at my arrival.—for I shall not give you a moments peace. I have so many things to ask about & talk about.—Everything goes on very well.—the SS Islands daily become more probable.—My cabin is more comfortable then I expected; & my only difficulty is about the disposal of my collection when I come back.—I have seen this very morning, Cap. Beaufort & had some talk on the subject.—There is one other disagreeable thing, but of this in future.—The ballance however is quite on the prosperous side.—Excuse this hasty letter & believe me dear Sir, with my best thanks, Yours ever most sincerely

                                                        Chas. Darwin.

LETTER 12

[*To:The Rev^d. Profes sor Henslow Cambridge*]

                                        28 Sept: 1831 [*Shrewsbury*]

My dear Henslow

I have received another parcel of the Phalli[1] from *Barmouth.*— & another jar of them, which I gathered the day before yesterday in a very damp shady wood: I am more than ever convinced that they are different species . . . —The Shropshire ones are, whiter, more conical & stiffer, than the Barmouth one: the ball more dark coloured, the cap has less jelly, & that not so dark coloured. They are all preserved in gin & *brine* owing to the want of more spirit. —I have sent some of the Leiodes.—Will you be kind enough when you [write *del*] send my goods to London.—you will enclose a piece of brick lapped up in the German fashion.—& mention likewise what sort of Lens Mr. Brown[2] recommended.— & lastly do not forget the introductions to Lowe[3] & Smith.—

I heard from Cap Fitzroy yesterday he gives me a week more of respite, & therefore I do not leave this place till the end of this

---

[1] Presumably *Phallus impudicus*, the Stinkhorn.

[2] Robert Brown the botanist and discoverer of the Brownian Movement, 1827: who always used single lenses. See also Letters 46, 47, 48 and 49.

[3] Possibly Richard Thomas Lowe, naturalist, 1802–74. English Chaplain at Madeira, 1832–54. Published *A Manual Flora of Madeira.*

week, & London on the 16th of October.—I wish indeed that [*the*] time was arrived, for I begin to be very anxious to start.— My Father is getting much more reconciled to the idea, as I knew he would as soon as he became accustomed to it.—

Believe me dear Henslow
Yours most sincerely
Chas. Darwin

Wednesday 28th.
Shrewsbury

LETTER 13

[*To: The Rev^d. Prof: Henslow Cambridge*]

17 Spring Gardens
Tuesday 18 Oct. 1831

My dear Henslow

   I called on your Brother yesterday & paid him the 7″ 12 [*£.7–12s*] which I owe you: & he told me that he was going to send a parcel to you; so that I seize the opportunity of writing to you on the subject of consignment [*first spelt consingement*].— I have talked to everybody: & you are my only recourse [*altered to resourse*]; if you will take charge, it will be doing me the greatest kindness.—The land carriage to Cambridge, will be as nothing compared to having some safe place to stow them; & what is more having somebody to see that they are safe.—I suppose plants & Birdsskins are the only things that give trouble: but I know you will do what is proper for them.—Will you give me as minute instructions about the directing as if you were writing to an Otaheite savage: or what will be better make a scetch of lid of box, & on it direct *precisely & every letter*, as if it was one I was going to send off from any remote place. About paying for them, I should think the best plan will be, after the arrival of one or two cases, to write to my Father, & he will place the sum to your account at any bank in Cambridge you may choose:—I will write to him on the subject: I am so very busy, as never was anything like it before: I have hardly time to look about me: I suppose we do not sail till November, so that I will, of course write to you from Devonport. Mr. Brown has been of great use to me, & most exceedingly pleasant & goodnatured.—

Your Brother must think me a regular practised swindler, for most unluckily I gave him the money *sealed up*; which most properly he opened when lo & behold there was 6 [£6] instead of 7″ 10: I am sure he will think for the future you are very rash to trust me.—Will you be kind enough to write to me, before I leave London on Sunday 16th. about consignements (*consignments*].

Believe me, my dear Henslow
Your ever sincerely obliged
Chas. Darwin.—

LETTER 14

To: C. Darwin Esqre, H.M.S. 'Beagle', Plymouth
From: J. S. Henslow
Postmark: Cambridge C 25 1831 26oC26 1831]

Cambridge 25 Oct 1831

My dear Darwin,

I have just received your letter about consignment with a statement of your attempt to cheat my Brother of 1£. Do look at the bill I see sent, for it runs in my head that you have read pounds for shillings and shillings for pounds & that you *ought* to have p^d him 12 .. 7 .. instead of 7 .. 12.—I can't be sure without searching after the Bills & putting the items together again—so that you may be right—As touching consignment I should think the best way is to do as Lowe does: direct as follows Revd Prof. Henslow. Cambridge

to the care of
J. W. Henslow Esqre. 12 Clements Inn

London, *Antipodes or England.*—
the part underlined being optional.
I intend a great addition to my clinometer by giving it a sight for calculating ∠ [*angular*] dist^{ces}. when I think it will comprize all

the Geologist wants. I have just met Watkins who is delighted to hear of your expedition. Downes is just returned from a short tour in Switzerland but what is that to a Fuegian—
The day after tomorrow our County election begins[1]—Mr Jenyns is chairman of Capt. Yorke's committee, proposed at one time to sleep at my house during the week, by which manouvre I had calculated upon getting my windows smashed—this would have been [as good as *added*] foraging in the enemies quarters— He however thinks it better to sleep at the Inn where the Committee sit—so I suppose I shall remain in peace unless the Anties get the upper hand & think me too much of a radical—I presume however that these things begin to cease from interesting you & ∴ leave you to your better meditations on Mermaids & Flying fish.—

Y⁸. affectionately
J. S. Henslow

[1] Henslow's involvement in Cambridge politics reveals his independent, fearless integrity. It was four years after the writing of this letter, that, during the Borough elections of 1835, his indignation at the underhand methods of the Conservative agents, led him to offer himself as nominal prosecutor against them on the proven charge of bribery. The story is given in L. Jenyns' *Memoir of the Rev. John Stevens Henslow*, 1862, pp. 60–4, from which I quote. 'Not only was the cry raised of "Henslow, common informer", whenever he appeared in the streets, but the same obnoxious words were placarded upon the walls in such large and enduring characters that even to this day (July, 1861) they are still distinctly visible in some places.' Dr Sydney Smith tells me that in the presentation copy of Jenyns' *Memoir* now in the Balfour Library, Cambridge, there is a note that the inscription on the walls of Corpus Christi was visible in 1881; and Dr S. Smith adds that in certain lights and in certain degrees of dampness it was still visible in 1964.
Lord Monteagle was one of the candidates, later to become Lord Chancellor. See Letter 51, in which Darwin thanks Henslow for obtaining the Government Grant for the publication of Z. See also footnote 2, p. 134.

LETTER 15

[*To: Rev^d. Prof: Henslow Cambridge*
Postmark: Devonport OC30 1831]

4 Clarence Baths 30th Oct. 1831
Devonport

My dear Henslow

Your letter has filled me with consternation—I never knew anything so stupid as my making such a mistake.—I have lost your letter, but I have no doubt you are right.—If I merely trusted to recollection I should [have thought *del*] yet think it was 7″ 12. But after the little swindling affair with your brother, I will not trust my own self: It is too bad of me to give you so much unnecessary trouble, but perhaps you can find out the prices of the principal things such as paper & binding books, & that will be sufficient to know which of the sums it is.—I can easily through my brother contrive to pay you.—I am very much obliged for your direction about consingment [*consignment*].—I believe most of the things will first go to Falmouth (where I must get an agent) & then to Cambridge.—I will tell my Father that you will send him a note with an account of what you pay for me.—and I do not think you will find him as careless as I am. —I hope to be able to assist the Philosoph. Society when I come back.—but from all I hear, I suppose I shall be in honor bound to give largely to British Museum,—Everything here goes on very prosperously. My beau ideal of a Captain is determined to make me as comfortable as he possibly can.—But the corner of the cabin, which is my private property, is most wofully small.—I have just room to turn round & that is all.—My friend the Doctor is an ass, but we jog on very amicably: at present he is in great tribulation, whether his cabin shall be painted French Grey or a dead white—I hear little except this subject from him.—The gun-room officers are a fine set of fellows, but rather rough, & their conversation is oftentimes so full of slang & sea phrases that it is as unintelligible as Hebrew to me.—Our Cabins are fitted most luxuriously with nothing except mahogany: in short, everything is going on as well [*as*] possible. I only wish they were a little faster.—I am afraid we shall not bona fide sail till 20th of next Month.—I want your advice de Mathematicus. After looking at my 11 books of Euclid, & first part of Algebra (including binomial theorem?) [*the rest of the letter written across the earlier sheets*] I may then begin Trigonometry after which must I begin Spherical? Are there any important parts in the 2 & 3 *parts* of Woods Algebra.—It is almost a shame to ask you, but I should be much obliged if you would write to me pretty soon.—You must be very busy; for if Messrs. Askew & Darrell have not got some fresh Brains in the vacation, they will give you some trouble:— What an important Epoch 1831 will be in my life.—taking ones degree, & starting for Patagonia are each in their respective ways memorable events. And you have been most instrumental in getting them both.—Remember me most kindly to Mrs. Henslow.— Leonard Jenyns & all other friends.—I often think of your good advice of taking all uncomfortable moments as matters of course: & not to be compared with all the lasting & solid advantages . . . —Indeed I never can do better than when I think of you & your advice

Ever yours my dear Henslow
Most affectionately
Chas. Darwin

You give me your brother's direction *12* Clements Inn. Is that right?

LETTER 16

[To: The Rev^d. Prof: Henslow Cambridge
Postmarks: Devonport No 15 1831 and 17 No 1831]

Nov. 15th 1831 Devonport

My dear Henslow,
    The orders are come down from the Admiralty & everything is finally settled—We positively sail the last day of this month &

I think before that time the Vessel will be ready.—She looks most beautiful, even a landsman must admire her, *we* think her the most perfect vessel ever turned out of the Dock yard.—one thing is certain no vessel has been fitted out so expensively & with so much care.—Everything that can be made so is of Mahogany, & nothing can exceed the neatness & beauty of all the accomodations.—The instructions are very general & leave a great deal to the Captains discretion & judgement, thus paying a substantial as well as many verbal compliments to him.—I will now give you an outline of the plans. 1st to Madeira or Canary (perhaps only

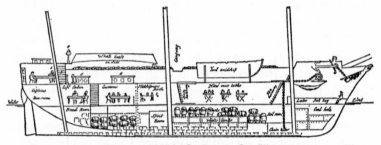

Contemporary diagram of H.M.S. *Beagle*. See Illustrations, p. viii.

the latter) Cape Verd, Fernando Noronha, Rio de Janeiro, Monte Video, then set to work at Patagonia, Terra del,[1] Falkland Islands, so as to consume about year & half. After this is completed to work our way Northward on [E *del*] W coast of S. America as far as Captain chooses, leaving time to take a good stretch across Pacific ocean—(taking some new course) New S Wales, Van Diemens land.—Some of E Indian Island[s], Cape of good hope, so home.—I grieve to say time is unlimited, but yet I hope we shall not exceed the 4 years.—No vessel ever left England with such a set of Chronometers,[2] viz 24, all very good ones.—In short everything is well, & I have only now to pray for the sickness to moderate its fierceness, & I shall do very well.—Yet I should not call it one of the very best opportunities for Nat Hist. that has ever occurred.—The absolute want of room is an evil, that noth-

[1] Tierra del Fuego often thus shortened.
[2] FitzRoy's special pride and Darwin's care on the voyage.

ing can surmount.—I think L. Jenyns did very wisely in not coming: that is, judging by my own feelings, for I am sure if I had left College some few years, or been those years older, I *never* could have endured it.—The officers (excepting the Captain) are like the freshest freshmen—that is in their manners: in everything else widely different—Remember me most kindly to him, & tell him if ever he dreams in the night of Palm trees he may in the morning comfort himself with the assurance that the voyage would not have suited him.—I am much obliged for your advice de Mathematicis. I suspect when I am struggling with a triangle I shall often wish myself in your room, & as for those wicked sulky surds, I do not know what I shall do without you to conjure them.—My time passes away very pleasantly. I know one or two pleasant people, foremost of whom is Mr. Thunder & Lightning Harris,[1] whom I daresay you have heard of. My chief employment is to go on board the Beagle & try to look as much like a sailor as ever I can.—I have no evidence of having taken in man, woman or child.—I am going to ask you to do one more commission & I trust it will be the last. When I was in Cambridge, I wrote to Mr. Ash asking [*him*] to send my college account to my Father, after having subtracted about 30£ for my furniture. This he has forgotten to do, & my Father has paid the bill, & I want to have the Furniture money transmitted to my Father. [though *del*] Perhaps you would be kind enough to speak to Mr. Ash. I have cost my Father so much money—I am quite ashamed of myself.—I will write once again before sailing & perhaps you will write to me before then. Remember me to Prof. Sedgwick & Mr Peacock.

Believe me Yours affectionately

Chas. Darwin

[1] William Snow Harris, 1791–1867. Nicknamed Thunder-and-Lightning Harris from his improvements to lightning-conductors, for which he was knighted in 1847; F.R.S. 1831. He met with much prejudice in England, and the Russian Navy adopted his invention before he could remove the objections from the minds of his own countrymen.

LETTER 17

*[To: C. Darwin Esq*r*, H.M.S. 'Beagle', Plymouth*
From: J. S. Henslow
Postmark: Oct 26 1831]

Cambridge 20 Nov [Oct] 1831

My dear Darwin,

As I have received the plates to Lowe's paper, I thought it w^d be a pity not to forward them to you, & so shall entrust them to L. Jenyns who goes to Town tomorrow to send by some Plymouth Coach—They may be of service in directing your attention whilst collecting land shells—In working your Surd. remember that you are operating merely in quantities with fractional indices & a little practice will enable you to see nothing so formidable in them as you seem to anticipate. Dress them up in this way & then compare them with the symbol $\sqrt{}$.

I have long since seen that the noble expedition upon which you are entering would have been no way fitted for L. Jenyns. With a little self denial on your part I am quite satisfied you must reap an abundant harvest of future satisfaction. If I may say so, one of your foibles is to take offence at rudeness of manners & any thing bordering upon ungentlemanlike behaviour, & I have observed such conduct often wounds your feelings far more deeply than you ought to allow it—I am no advocate for rudeness God forbid, & still less for any thing dishonourable but we must make abundant allowances for mal-education, early contamination, & vulgar feelings, if we really intend to pass smoothly through life —& I therefore exhort you sincerely & affectionately never to feel offended at any of the coarse or vulgar behaviour you will infallibly be subjected to among your comrades—Take St James's advice & bridle your tongue when in [*it*] burns with some merited rebuke, & the impatient feelings which these evils must generate in your own [feeling *del*] polished mind will gradually subside & you will be satisfied with the real & stirling worth you will not fail to find beneath many a rough surface. I have all along preached to you on the necessity of submitting to evils of various descriptions & when you come back I hope to have my lessons repeated to myself (if I should appear to need them) under the positive advanges [*advantages*] of long & experienced trial. I am quite sure that you are the *right* man for the expedition you have undertaken, & that there is in you every thing that is wanted to make it turn out favorably—I am not yet very old, but I have a few more years experience over my head, & I have ever found the advantage of accommodating myself to circumstances. It is wonderful how soon a little submission conquers an evil & then all goes on smoothly.

Believe me ever Y^r. affect^y. J. S. Henslow (Write again)

LETTER 18

[*To: The Rev^d. Prof: Henslow Cambridge*
Postmarks: Devonport Dec 4 1831, and 5 DE 5 1831]

Devonport
December 3rd. 1831

My dear Henslow

It is now late in the evening, & tonight I am going to sleep on board.—On Monday we most certainly sail, so you may guess in what a desperate state of confusion we are all in.—If you were to hear the various exclamations of the officers, you would suppose we had scarcely had a weeks notice.—I am just in the same way, taken all *aback*: & in such a bustle I hardly know what to do.—The number of things to be done is infinite. I look forward even to sea sickness with something like satisfaction; anything must be better than this state of anxiety.—I am very much obliged for your last kind & affectionate letter.—I always like advice from you; and no one whom I have the luck to know is more capable of giving it than yourself.—Recollect, when you write, that I am a sort of protegé of yours, & that it is your bounden duty to lecture me.—I will now give you my direction: it is, at first, Rio; but if you will send me letter on first Tuesday (when packet sails) in February, directed to Monte Video, it will give me very great pleasure. I shall so much enjoy hearing a little

Cambridge news.—Poor dear old Alma Mater. I am a very worthy son in as far as affection goes.—I have little more to write about, I shall be very glad to have some memorial of Ramsay.—My very short acquaintance with him appears like a dream.—which has left many melancholy yet pleasant recollections.—I cannot end this, without telling you how cordially I feel grateful for the kindness you have shown me during my Cambridge life.—Much of the pleasure & utility which I may have derived from it is owing to you.—I long for the time when we shall again meet; & till then believe me, my dear Henslow,

Your affectionate & obliged friend
Chas. Darwin

Remember me most kindly to those who take any interest in me.—

LETTER 19

[To: The Rev^d. Prof: Henslow Cambridge
No Postmark]

Rio de Janeiro. May 18th 1832

My dear Henslow.—

I have delayed writing to you till this period as I was determined to have a fair trial of the voyage. I have so many things to write about, that my head is as full of oddly assorted ideas, as a bottle on the table is with animals.—You being my chief Lord of the Admiralty, must excuse this letter being full of my's & I's.— After our two attempts to put to sea in spite of the SWly gales, the time at Plymouth passed away very unpleasantly.—I would have written, only I had nothing to say, excepting what had better be left unsaid: so that I only wrote to Shrewsbury.[1]—At length we started from Plymouth on the 27th of December with a prosper-

---

[1] I can find no trace of this letter describing his misery. The passage in his *Autobiography* (ed. Nora Barlow, Collins, 1958, p. 79) is here worth quoting: 'These two months at Plymouth were the most miserable I ever spent, though I exerted myself in various ways. I was out of spirits at the thoughts of leaving all

Charles Darwin, 1840.
An unsigned sketch for the well-known portrait by
George Richmond, found in the cellars of the Cambridge
Botany School in 1929

Captain Robert FitzRoy,
Commander of H.M.S. *Beagle*, *c.* 1836

ous wind which has lasted during our whole voyage:—The two little peeps at sea-sick misery gave me but a faint idea of what I was going to undergo.—Till arriving at Teneriffe (we did not touch at Madeira) I was scarcely out of my hammock & really suffered more than you could well imagine from such a cause.—At Santa Cruz, whilst looking amongst the clouds for the Peak & repeating to myself Humboldt's sublime descriptions, it was announced we must perform 12 days strict quarantine.—We had made a short passage, so "Up Jib" & away for St Jago.—You will say all this sounds very bad, & so it was: but from that to the present time it has been nearly one scene of continual enjoyment.—A net over the stern kept me at full work, till we arrived at St Jago:[1] here we spent three most delightful weeks. The geology was preeminently interesting & I believe quite new: there are some facts on a large scale of upraised coast (which is an excellent epoch for all the Volcanic rocks to date from) [& I *del*] that would interest Mr. Lyell.—One great source of perplexity to me is an utter ignorance whether I note the right facts & whether they are of sufficient importance to interest others.—In the one thing collecting, I cannot go wrong.—St Jago is singularly barren & produces few plants or insects.—so that my hammer was my usual companion & in its company most delightful hours I spent. —On the coast I collected many marine animals chiefly gasteropodous (I think [many *del*] some new).—I examined pretty accurately a Caryophillea[2] [*corrected to Caryophyllea*] & if my eyes were not bewitched former descriptions have not the slightest resemblance to the animal.—I took several specimens of an Octopus

---

my family and friends for so long a time, and the weather seemed to me inexpressibly gloomy. I was also troubled with palpitations and pain about the heart, and like many a young ignorant man, especially one with a smattering of medical knowledge, was convinced that I had heart disease.' This, I believe, is the first mention of any heart symptoms. For the second, see Letters 52 and 54 (pp. 136 and 138) written after his return home, when he was again in a state of unusual tension and anxiety.

[1] Cape Verde Islands, memorable as the first testing-ground for Darwin's geological theories after reading Charles Lyell. Here also Darwin made his first geological collections.

[2] Darwin's first mention of Corallines. See later, Letter 26, p. 72.

which possessed a most marvellous power of changing its colours:
[fa *del*] equalling any chamaelion, & evidently accommodating
the changes to the colour of the ground which it passed over.—
yellowish green, dark brown & red were the prevailing colours:
this fact appears to be new, as far as I can find out.—Geology &
the invertebrate animals will be my chief object of pursuit through
the whole voyage.—We then sailed for Bahia, & touched at the
rock of St Paul.—This is a Serpentine formation.—Is it not the
only island in the Atlantic which is not *Volcanic*?[1]—We likewise
staid a few hours at Fernando Noronha; a tremendous surf was
running, so that a boat was swamped, & the Captain would not
wait.—I find my life on board, when we are in blue water most
delightful; so very comfortable & quiet: it is almost impossible to
be idle, & that for me is saying a good deal. Nobody could
possibly be better fitted out in every respect for collecting than I
am: many cooks have not spoiled the broth this time; Mr Browne's
little hint about microscopes etc have been invaluable.—I am
well off in books. the Dic: Class:[2] is *most useful.*—If you should
think of anything or book that would be useful to me: if you
would write one line E. Darwin Whyndham Club St James St.—
He will procure them & send them with some other things to
Monte Video, which for the next year will be my head quarters.
—Touching at the Abrolhos[3] we arrived here[4] on April 4th,

[1] Dr F. W. Dunning of the Geological Survey and Museum has given me an
estimation of Darwin's views in the light of modern knowledge, which I here
quote with grateful acknowledgment: 'Darwin was correct in identifying the St
Peter and St Paul's Rocks (to give them their proper title) as serpentine. It is also
true to say that they are not volcanic in the sense of not being formed by out-
pourings of lava at the surface. The St Peter and St Paul's Rocks are the centre of
intense interest today, for it appears from isotope age determinations that they
may represent the primordial material of the Earth's mantle, this being the first
time that material as old as the Earth itself (4,500 million years) has been recognised. The serpentine is not, however, mantle material in its original form; it has
been hydrated, sheared and intruded near the surface. According to H. H. Hess, it
is the material that composes the so-called "basalt layer" of the oceanic crust.'

[2] *Dictionnaire classique d'Histoire naturelle*, Tome 1–17, 1822–31. This and
Tome 18 of *Dictionnaire des Sciences Naturelles* are catalogued in *The Library of
C. Darwin*, 1908.

[3] In Henslow's pamphlet with excerpts from Darwin's letters, published by the
Cam. Phil. Soc., 1835, he gives Abrothos for Abrolhos. The reason is clear, for in
the MS the 'l' appears crossed.   [4] Rio de Janeiro.

when amongst others I received your most kind letter: you may rely on it, during the evening, I thought of the many most happy hours I have spent with you in Cambridge.—I am now living at Botofogo, a village about a league from the city, & shall be able to remain [some *del*] a month longer.—The Beagle has gone back to Bahia, & will pick me up on its return. There is a most important error in the longitude of S America, to settle which this second trip has been undertaken.—Our Chronometers at least 16 of them, are going superbly: none on record ever have gone at all like them. A few days after arriving I started on an expedition of 150 miles to Rio Macaò, which lasted 18 days.— Here I first saw a Tropical forest in all its sublime grandeur.— Nothing but the reality can give any idea, how wonderful, how magnificent, the scene is.—If I was to specify any one thing I should give the preeminence to the host of parasitical plants.— Your engraving is exactly true, but underates, rather than exagerates the luxuriance.—I never experienced such intense delight.— I formerly admired Humboldt, I now almost adore him; he alone gives any notion, of the feelings which are raised in the mind on first entering the Tropics.—I am now collecting fresh-water & land animals: if what was told me in London is true viz that there are no small insects in the collections from the Tropics.—I tell Entomologists to look out & have their pens ready for describing. —I have taken as minute (if not more so) as in England, Hydropori, Hygroti, Hydrobii, Pselaphi, Staphylini, Curculio, Bembididous insects etc etc.—It is exceedingly interesting observing[1] the difference of genera & species from those which I know, it is however much less than I had expected. I am at present red-hot with Spiders, they are very interesting, & if I am not mistaken I have already taken some new genera.—I shall have a large box to send [home *del*] very soon to Cambridge, & with that I will mention some more Natural History particulars.—The Captain does everything in his power to assist me, & we get on very well. —but I thank my better fortune he has not made me a renegade to Whig principles: I would not be a Tory, if it was merely

[1] Altered to 'to observe', probably by Henslow.

on account of their cold hearts about that scandal to Christian Nations, Slavery.—I am very good friends with all the officers; & as for the Doctor he has gone back to England.—as he chose to make himself disagreeable to the Captain & to Wickham.—He was a philosopher of rather an antient date; at St Jago by his own account he made *general* remarks during the first fortnight & collected particular facts during the last.—I have just returned from a walk & as a specimen how little the insects are know[n].—Noterus, according to Dic. Class. contains solely 3 European species, I, in one hawl of my net took five distinct species.—is this not quite extraordinary?—June 16th—I have determined not to send a box till we arrive at Monte Video.—it is too great a loss of time both for Carpenters & myself to pack up whilst in harbor. —I am afraid when I do send it, you will be disappointed, not having skins of birds & but very few plants, & geological specimens small: the rest of the things in bulk make very little show.— I received a letter from Herbert,[1] stating that you have a vol: of Dic Class—Will you send it to Whyndham Club.—I suppose you [will *del*] are at this moment in some seaport with your pupils. —I hope for their & your sake, that there will be but few rainy [days *del*] mathematical days.—How I should enjoy one week with you: quite as much as you would one in the glorious Tropics.— We sail for Monte Video at the end of this month (June) so that I shall have been here nearly 3 months.—this has been very lucky for me.—as it will be some considerable period before we again cross the Tropics.—I am sometimes afraid I shall never be able to hold out for the whole voyage. I believe 5 years is the shortest period it will consume.—The mind requires a little case-hardening, before it can calmly look at such an interval of separation from all friends.—Remember me most kindly to Mrs Henslow & the two Signoritas; also to L. Jenyns, Mr Dawes & Mr Peacock.— Tell Prof: Sedgwick he does not know how much I am indebted to him for the Welch expedition,—it has given me an interest in

---

[1] John Maurice Herbert, his musical Cambridge friend, who took a high Wrangler's degree and became County Court Judge of Cardiff.

geology—which I would not give up for any consideration.—I do not think I ever spent a more delightful three weeks, than in pounding the NW mountains.—I look forward to the Geology about M. Video—as I hear there are slate [*formations?*] there. so I presume in that district I shall find the junction of the Pampas of the enormous granite formation of Brazils.—At Bahia the Pegmatite & gneiss in beds had same direction as observed by Humboldt prevailing over Columbia, distant 1300 miles: is it not wonderful?—M. Video will be for long time my direction:—I hope you will write again to me.—there is nobody, from whom I like receiving advice so much as from you.—I shall be much obliged if you will get one of the engravings of poor Mr Ramsay & keep it for me.—Excuse this almost unintelligible letter & believe me dear Henslow—with the warmest feelings of respect & friendship

Yours affectionately
Chas Darwin

June 16th

P.S. I found the other day a beautiful Hymenophallus. (but broke it to pieces in bringing home) & with it an accompanying Leiodes. —a most perfect copy of the Barmouth specimen.—

LETTER 20

[*To: The Revᵈ. Prof: Henslow Cambridge England*
Postmark: FPO NO 28 1832. Also: C NO 28 1832
The letter had taken three and a half months to reach England]

15 Aug 1832 Monte Video

My dear Henslow

We are now beating up the Rio Plata, & I take the opportunity of beginning a letter to you.—I did not send off the specimens from R Janeiro; as I grudged the time it would take to pack them up.—They are now ready to be sent off, & most probably by the Packet.—If so they go to Falmouth (where C. FitzRoy has made arrangements) & so will not trouble your Brothers agent in

London.—When I left England,—I was not fully aware how essential a kindness you offered me, when you undertook to receive my boxes.—I do not know what I should do without such headquarters.—And now for an apologetical prose about my collection.—I am afraid you will say it is very small,—but I have not been idle & you must recollect that in lower tribes, what a very small show hundreds of species make.—The box contains a good many geological specimens.—I am well aware that the greater number are too small.—But I maintain that no person has a right to accuse me, till he has tried carrying rocks under a Tropical sun.—[All *del*] I have endeavoured to get specimens of every variety of rock, & have written notes upon all.—If you think it worth your while to examine any of them, I shall be *very* glad of some mineralogical information, especially in any numbers between 1 & 254, which include St Jago rocks.—By my Catalogue,[1] I shall know which you may refer to.—As for my Plants. "pudet pigetque mihi." All I can say is that when objects are present which I can observe & particularize about, I cannot summon resolution to collect where I know nothing.—

It is positively distressing to walk in the glorious forest, amidst such treasures, & feel they are all thrown away upon one.—My collection from the Abrolhos is interesting as I suspect it nearly contains the whole flowering Vegetation, & indeed from extreme sterility the same may almost be said of St. Jago.—I have sent home 4 bottles with animals in spirits I have three more, but would not send them till I had a fourth.—I shall be anxious to know how they fare.—I made an enormous collection of Arachnidae at Rio.—Also a good many small beetles in pill-boxes: but it is not the best time of year for the latter.—As I have only [half *del*] ¾ of a case of Diptera etc I have not sent them.—Amongst the lower animals, nothing has so much interested me as finding 2 species of elegantly coloured true Planariae, inhabiting the dry forest! The false relation they bear to Snails is the most extraordinary thing of the kind I have ever seen.—In the same genus

[1] He kept a separate catalogue for all his geological specimens, now at Down House. See also Appendix III, p. 230.

(or more truly family) some of the marine species possess an organization so marvellous—that I can scarcely credit my eyesight.—Everyone has heard of the discoloured streaks of water [under *del*] in the Equatorial regions.—One I examined was owing to the presence of such minute Oscillaria that in each square inch of surface there must have been at least [from *del*] one hundred thousand present.—After this I had better be silent,—for you will think me a Baron Munchausen[1] amongst Naturalists.—Most assuredly I might collect a far greater number of specimens of Invertebrate animals if I took less time over each: But I have come to the conclusion that 2 animals with their original colour & shape noted down, will be more valuable to Naturalists than 6 with only dates & place.—I hope you will send me your criticisms about my collection; & it will be my endeavour that nothing you say shall be lost on me.—I would send home my writing with my specimens, only I find I have so repeatedly occasion to refer back, that it would be a serious loss to me.—I cannot conclude about my collections, without adding that I implicitly trust in you, keeping an exact account against all the expense of *boxes etc etc.*— At this present minute we are at anchor in the mouth of the river: & such a strange scene as it is.—Everything is in flames.—the sky with lightning.—the water with luminous particles, & even the very masts are pointed with a blue flame.—I expect great interest in scouring over the plains of M Video, yet I look back with regret to the Tropics, that magic line to all Naturalists.— The delight of sitting on a decaying trunk amidst the quiet gloom of the forest is unspeakable & never to be forgotten.—How often have I then wished for you—when I see a Banana, I well recollect admiring them with you in Cambridge.—little did I then think how soon I should eat their fruit.—

August 15th. In a few days the Box will go by the Emulous Packet (Captn Cooke) to Falmouth & will be forwarded to you. —This letter goes the same way so that if in course of due time

[1] *The Adventures of Baron von Münchausen*, a small satirical volume of exaggerated adventure stories, compiled by Rudolf Erich Raspe and first published in 1785. A new edition with illustrations by Rowlandson, 1809, was perhaps the edition known to C.D.

you do not receive the box, will you be kind enough to write to Falmouth.—We have been here (Monte Video) for some time; but owing to bad weather & continual fighting on shore have scarcely ever been able to walk in the country.—I have collected during the last month nothing.—But today I have been out & returned like Noahs ark,—with animals of all sorts.—I have to-day to my astonishment found 2 *Planariae* living under dry stones. Ask L. Jenyns if he has ever heard of this fact. I also found a most curious snail & Spiders, beetles, snakes, scorpions ad libitum. And to conclude shot a Cavia weighing a cwt:—On Friday we sail for the Rio Negro, & then will commence our real wild work.—I look forward with dread to the wet stormy regions of the South.—But after so much pleasure I must put up with some sea-sickness & misery.—Remember me most kindly to everybody & believe me, my dear Henslow.

Yours affectionately
Chas. Darwin

Monte Video. August 15th.—

LETTER 21

[*To:The Rev^d. Prof: Henslow Cambridge*
No Postmark.]

Monte Video 24 Nov 1832

My dear Henslow,

We arrived here on the 24th of Octob: after our first cruize on the coast of Patagonia: North of the Rio Negro we fell in with some little Schooners employed in sealing; to save the loss of time in surveying the intricate mass of banks, Capt. FitzRoy has hired two of them & has put officers in them.[1]—It took us nearly a month fitting them out; as soon as this was finished we came back here, & are now preparing for a long cruize to the South.—I expect to find the wild mountainous country of Terra del very interesting; & after the coast of Patagonia I shall thoroughly

[1] Captain FitzRoy undertook the hire of the schooners at his own expense in his zeal for the furtherance of the survey, but without the sanction of the Admiralty. See *D*, pp. 99, 106. Notes 21, 29, 45.

enjoy it.—I had hoped for the credit of dame Nature, no such country [as this last *added*] existed; in sad reality we coasted along 240 miles of sand hillocks; I never knew before, what a horrid ugly object a sand hillock is:—The famed country of the Rio Plata in my opinion is not much better; an enormous brackish river bounded by an interminable green plain, is enough to make any naturalist groan. So hurrah for Cape Horn & the land of storms.—Now that I have had my growl out, which is a priviledge *sailors* take on all occasions, I will turn the tables & give an account of my doings in Nat: History.—I must have one more growl, by ill luck the French government has sent one of its Collectors to the Rio Negro.—where he has been working for the last six months, & is now gone round the Horn.—So that I am very selfishly afraid he will get the cream of all the good things before me.—As I have nobody to talk to about my luck & ill luck in collecting, I am determined to vent it all upon you.—I have been very lucky with fossil bones; I have fragments of at least 6 distinct animals; as many of them are teeth I trust, shattered & rolled as they have been, they will be recognised. I have paid *all the attention*, I am *capable* of, to their geological site; but of course it is too long a story for here.—1st [I have *del*] the Tarsi & metatarsi very perfect of a Cavia: 2nd the upper jaw & head of some very large animal with 4 square hollow molars.—& the head greatly produced in front.—I at first thought it [was *del*] belonged either to the Megalonyx or Megatherium.—in confirmation of this, in the same formation I found a large surface of the osseous polygonal plates, which "late observations" (what are they?) show belong to the Megatherium.—Immediately I saw them I thought they must belong to an enormous Armadillo, living species of which genus are so abundant here:[1] 3rd The lower jaw of some large animal, which from the molar teeth I should think belonged to the Edentata: 4th some [very *del*] large molar teeth, which in some respects would seem to belong to an enormous

[1] The first mention of Darwin's recognition of the living and long extinct fossil armadillos. The deep impression was immediate, showing the trend of his thoughts.

Rodentia; 5th, also some smaller teeth belonging to the same order: etc etc.—If it interests you sufficiently to unpack them, I shall be *very curious* to hear something about them:—*Care must be taken*, in this case, not to confuse the tallies.—They are mingled with marine shells, which appear to me identical with what now exist.—But since they were deposited in their beds, several geological changes have taken place in the country.—So much for the dead & now for the living.—there is a poor specimen of a bird, which to my unornithological eyes, appears to be a happy mixture of a lark pidgeon & snipe (No. 710) [*added bracketed above line*].[1]—Mr Mac Leay himself never imagined such an inosculating creature.—[2] I suppose it will turn out to be some well-

[1] This number refers to the number in the *Beagle* notebook labelled *Ornithology*, in which he entered all his bird observations. The numbers were consecutive for all biological specimens, the geological specimens having a separate series. See *Ornithological Notes, Bull. B.M. (N.H.)* Vol. 2, No. 7, 1963.

[2] In *Z.*, Part III, *Ornithology*, published 1841, the 'inosculating bird' has become *Tinochorus rumicivorus*. Darwin writes: 'In the Appendix, Mr. Eyton has given an anatomical description of this bird, which partly confirms that affinity both to the Grallatores and Razores, which is so remarkable in its habits and external appearance.' This bird, No. 710 in Darwin's *Ornithological Notes* of the voyage, marked the turning point in Darwin's work on birds. It was at Monte Video, in the summer of 1832, that he took over the writing of these notes from his amanuensis, and noted of 710: 'In its habits & structure it seems allied to the two Genera Scolopax & Perdrix . . . from their long scapulars, when on the wing, they fly just like snipes'. He then describes their behaviour and habits.

William Sharp Macleay, 1792–1865, gained a transient fame for his Quinary System of classification, described in *Horae Entomologiae* in 1819 and 1821, and later extended by Vigors and Swainson. This mystical desire to represent the works of creation in diagrammatic form of adjacent circles, soon fell into disrepute; it was from Macleay that Darwin must have derived the word 'inosculating'. Macleay wrote, p. 37: 'These genera I propose to call *osculantia*, from their occurring as it were at the point where the circles touch one another.' This source of Darwin's use of the word 'inosculating' is of interest in Eiseley's argument on Darwin's lack of acknowledgment of his debt to Edward Blyth. See Loren C. Eiseley, *Proc. Am. Phil. Soc.*, Vol. 103, No. 1, Feb. 1959, pp. 100 and 103, where Eiseley is following the trail of E. Blyth's influence on Darwin. Eiseley writes: 'This trail begins to be discernible in the Darwin Note-book of 1836 with the curious word "inosculate". It is a word which has never had a wide circulation, and which is not to be found in Darwin's vocabulary before this time.' Eiseley believed that Darwin followed Blyth in the use of this word. Darwin's use of the word in 1832 in direct conjunction with Macleay's name, refutes this argument. Blyth also had studied Macleay's Quinary System, and also probably derived the word direct from Macleay.

See *Ornithological Notes, Bull. B.M. (N.H.)*, Vol. 2, No. 7, 1963, and Dr Sydney Smith, Linnean Soc., 1962. Also Dr Sydney Smith, *Linnean Papers*, 1962.

know[n] bird, although it has quite baffled me.—I have taken some interesting amphibia; a fine Bipes; a new Trigonocephalus beautifully connecting in its habits Crotalus & Viperus: & plenty of new (as far as my knowledge goes) Saurians.—As for one little toad; I hope it may be new, that it may be christened "diabolicus". —Milton must allude to this very individual, when he talks of "squat like [a] toad",[1] its colours are by Werner, *ink black, Vermilion red & buff orange.*—It has been a splendid cruize for me in Nat: History.—Amongst the pelagic Crustaceae, some new & curious genera.—In the Zoophites some interesting animals.—as for one Flustra, if I had not the specimen to back me up, nobody would believe in its most anomolous structure.—But as for novelty all this is nothing to a family of pelagic animals; which at first sight appear like Medusa, but are really highly organized.—I have examined them repeatedly, & certainly from their structure, it would be impossible to place them in any existing order.—Perhaps Salpa is the nearest animal; although the transparency of the body is nearly the only character they have in common.—All this may be said of another animal, although of a much simpler structure.—I think the dried plants nearly contain all which were then [Bahia Blanca *added*] flowering. All the specimens will be packed in casks—I think there will be three: (before sending [this letter *added*] I will specify dates, etc etc).—I am afraid you will groan or rather the floor of the Lecture room will, when the casks arrive. —Without you I should be utterly undone.—The small cask contains fish; will you open it to see how the spirit has stood the evaporation of the Tropics.—

On board the Ship everything goes on as well as possible, the only drawback is the fearful length of time between this & day of our return.—I do not see any limits to it: one year is nearly completed & the second will be so before we even leave the East coast of S America.—And then our voyage may be said really to have commenced.—I know not, how I shall be able to endure it. —The frequency with which I think of all the happy hours I have

---

[1] *Paradise Lost*, Bk. IV, l. 799. Darwin carried a volume of Milton in his pocket on his inland expeditions.

spent at Shrewsbury & Cambridge, is rather ominous.—I trust everything to time & fate & will feel my way as I go on:— [Nov. 24th *added*] We have been at Buenos Ayres for a week.— it is a fine large city; but such a country; everything is mud: you can go no where, you can do nothing for mud.—In the city [*I*] obtained much information about the banks of the Uruguay.—I hear of Limestone with shells, & beds of shells in every direction. —I hope when we winter in the Plata to have a most interesting Geological excursion in that country.—I purchased fragments (No^{rs} : 837 & 8) of some enormous bones; which I was assured belonged to the former giants!!—I also procured some seeds.—I do not know whether they are worth your accepting; if you think so, I will get some more:—they are in the box: I have sent to you by the Duke of York Packet, commanded by Lieu: Snell to Falmouth.—two large casks, containing fossil bones.—a small cask with fish, & a box containing skins, spirit bottle etc & pill-boxes with beetles.—Would you be kind enough as to open these latter, as they are apt to become mouldy.—With the exceptions of the bones, the rest of my collection looks very scanty. Recollect how great a proportion of time is spent at sea. I am always anxious to hear in what state my things come & any criticisms about quantity or kind of specimens.—In the smaller cask is part of a large head, the anterior portions of which are in the other large one.—The packet has arrived & I am in a great bustle: you will not hear from me for some months: Till then believe me, my dear Henslow,

Yours very truly obliged, Chas Darwin.— Remember me most kindly to Mrs. Henslow.—

LETTER 22

[*To: C. Darwin Esqr, H.M.S. 'Beagle', Monte Video (or elsewhere)*
From: J. S. Henslow
No postmark]

Cambridge 15 Jany 1832
[*should be 1833*]

My dear Darwin,

I shall begin a letter to you lest something or other should persuade me to defer it till it becomes too late for the next packet—
Wood & I had intended writing by the Decr. packet, but just as
[*I*] was about to do so your letter arrived stating that a Box was
on its road, so I thought I had better delay till I had seen its contents. It is now here & every thing has travelled well. I shall however proceed by rule & answer your two letters first & then come
to the Box. The 1st date of your first letter is May 18. & this I
received at Cambridge in June, [just as *del*] no, it was sent me
from Cambridge in July, to Weymouth where I was spending the
summer with my family and two pupils in exploring the geology
etc etc of that neighbourhood, & a capable [*capital?*] ramble we
had. I stopped at Oxford in [*on*] my way there, where the British
Association had assembled for a week's scientific discussion & a
delightful time it was. Next summer this society is to meet in
Cambridge. When in Oxford I received a letter from the L^d
Chancellor giving me a small living in Berksh: about 14 miles
from Oxford, of course I do not reside, as I never mean to quit
Cambridge without something very extraordinary should happen.[1] I never mean to leave it for lucres sake. We returned to
Cambridge in Oct^r. & have had the bustle of the Election to go
thru'. We could make nothing of any attempt to squeeze a Whig
in for the University so gave it up. We have got 2 Whigs for the
town and 2 Whigs & one Tory for the County. But the papers
will tell you all this. At this moment I am examiner in Paley &
in one hour have to attend in the Senate house. Now for a re-
vision of your letters—I would not bother myself about whether
I were right or wrong in noting such & such facts about Geology

[1] See Letter 33, p. 89.

—note all that *may* be useful—most of all, the relative positions of rocks giving a little sketch thus. No. 1 (specimen (a)) about 10 feet thick, pretty uniform in character—No. 2 (specn. b.c.) variable etc. etc.

When Sedgwick returns we will look over your specimens & I will send you our joint report—they seem quite *large* enough! I myself caught an Octopus at Weymouth this summer & observed the change of color whenever I opened the tin box in which I put it, but not in such great perfection as you seem to have done. The fact is not new, but any fresh observations will be highly important. Quœre if a *serpentine rock* be not the produce of volcanic baking of a chloritic slate? The rock of St Paul *may* not be an exception to the usual character of the Isl^s. of the Atlantic. I have got the description of the plates to the Dict. Classique & will send it where you direct. Your account of the Tropical forest is delightful, I can't help envying you. So far from being disappointed with the Box—I think you have done wonders—as I know you do not confine yourself to collecting, but are careful to describe. Most of the plants are very desirable to *me*. Avoid sending *scraps*. Make the specimens as perfect as you can, *root, flowers* & *leaves* & you can't do wrong. In large ferns & leaves fold them back upon themselves on *one* side of the specimen & they will get into a proper sized paper. *Don't* trouble yourself to stitch them—for the [*they*] really travel better without it, and a single label *per month* to those of the same place is enough except you have plenty of spare time or spare hands to write more. L. Jenyns does not know what to make of your land Planariae. Do you mistake for such the curious Genus, "Oncidium" allied to slug, of which a fig. is given in Linn. Transact. & one not the marine species also *mollusca*, perhaps Doris &

other genera—Specimens & observations upon these wd. be
highly interesting. If you could get hold of Cuvier's *Anatomie des
Mollusques,* you wd. find it very useful but I fear it is out of print
—I will tell your Brother to enquire at Truttles. Watkins has
received your letter—And now for the Box—Lowe *under packs*
Darwin *overpacks*—The latter is in fault on the right side. You
need not make quite so great a parade of tow & paper for the
geolog. specimens, as they travel very well provided they be each
wrapped up *german fashion* & closely stowed—but *above all
things* don't put tow round *anything* before you have first wrapped
it up in a piece of thin paper—It is impossible to clear away the
fibres of the tow from some of your specimens without injuring
them.—an excellent crab has lost all its legs, & an Echinus $\frac{1}{2}$ its
spines by this error. I don't think however that any other specimens besides these 2 have been at all injured. Another caution I
wd. give is to place the number on the specimen always inside &
never outside the cover. The moisture & friction have rubbed off
one or two—& I can't replace them. I shall thoroughly dry the
different perishable commodities & then put them in pasteboard
boxes with camphor & paste over the edges, & place them in my
study or some very dry place. The heavy material I shall send to
my lecture room, so soon as it is again habitable—for at present
we are all in confusion—building a large Museum & lecture room
& private rooms adjoining mine, for Clark & Cumming—I must
now leave off for the Senate house & put this bye till I can find
a few more minutes to conclude it.

Jany. 21. The Exam^n is over & no X^ts. [*Christ's*] man plucked—
I don't know whether you were acquainted with the men of this
y^r. (except Downes who is No. 26) or I wd send you their names
—The Capt. is Laffer [?] of X^ts.—I have just been putting bye the
perishable articles in the way I said—*Birds*—several have no
labels—the best way is to tie the label to their legs—One has its
tail feathers crumpled by being bent from bad packing—the rest
in good order—*Quad*^s. [*Quadrupeds*] The large one capital, the
two mice rather mouldy—Pack up an infinite quantity more of

land & freshwater shells, they must be nearly all new—The minute Insects most excellent—what work you will have—You know better than [me *del*] I whether it is not dangerous to their antennae & legs to pack them in cotton. I suppose if moistened in vapour they may be taken out quite safe.—The Lichens are *good things* as scarcely any one troubles himself to send them home— For goodness sake what is No. 223 it looks like the remains of an electric explosion, a mere mass of soot—something very curious I daresay—W^d. it not be a good precautionary measure to transmit to England a copy of your memoranda, with your next packet? I know it is a dull job to copy out such matters—but it is highly expedient to avoid the chance of losing your notes by sending home a duplicate—Every individual specimen once arrived here becomes an object of great interest, & tho' you were to send home 10 times as much as you do, yet when you arrive you will often think & wish how you might have [& had] sent home 100 times as much! things which seemed such rubbish— but now so valuable—However no one can possibly say you have not been active—& that your box is not capital. I shall not wait for Sedgwick's return before I send this but must give you an account of the Geol. spec^s. in the next—I shall now forward this with the vol. of the Dict. Class. to your Brother & wish you a continuance of good success. I have no fears of your being tired of the expedition whilst you continue to meet with such as you have hitherto, & hope your spirits will not fail you in those dull moments which must occasionally intervene, during the progress of so long an undertaking. Downes & other friends have begged me to remember them to you most kindly & affectionately & Mrs. Henslow adds her best wishes—Mine you well know are ever with you & I need not add that you cd believe me

Most affect^ly. & sincerely y^r.

J. S. Henslow

My 3 children are well—& my boy is growing a very fine fellow —An increase expected next June—We are in Mourning for Mrs Henslow's Mother.

'Fuegian wigwams at Hope Harbour in the Magdalen Channel'

Voyages of the Beagle, vol. I, p. 126

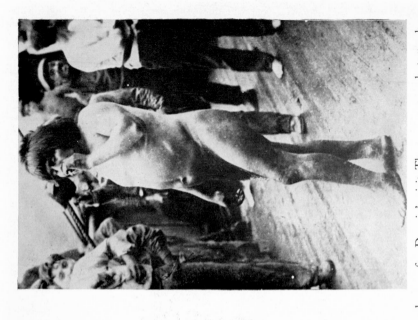

Fuegian natives in the Straits of Magellan, nearly one hundred years after Darwin's visit. The anonymous photographer walked seven miles over rugged country before finding the native camp. His ship was anchored off Ushuaia in the Beagle Channel; on the rocks the word 'Beagle' was seen with other roughly daubed ships' names.

LETTER 23

[*To: The Rev^d. Prof: Henslow*
No postmark
From: Erasmus Darwin, Charles's brother]

24 Regent St
Jan 23. 1833

Dear Sir

I have received your parcel containing a book etc and a letter for my Brother. I will forward them by the first opportunity, and will follow your suggestion in endeavouring to obtain the *Anatomie des Mollusques* which I do not think he at present has.

I feel very much obliged to you for the two letters you are so good as to send. I have had great pleasure in reading them, and will gladly make use of your permission to send them home, and will take care that they are returned to you.

I do not know whether I can be of any assistance to you either in receiving or forwarding the Boxes which my Brother may send to you, and can only beg that you will make any use of me that may be convenient

I remain yours
Sincerely obliged
E. Darwin

24 Regent St—
P.S. My Brother mentions in his letter that his Box is to be forwarded through Capt. Fitz Roy's Agent at Falmouth. The former Agent of Capt Fitz Roy (I forget his name) failed and I had in consequence considerable difficulty in sending out some books.

If you should happen to know the address of the present Agent who forwarded the Box, I should feel exceedingly obliged to you if you could send it to me. I should not venture to give you so much trouble if I were not so well acquainted with all your kindness to my Brother.

F

LETTER 24

[*To: The Rev*ᵈ. *Professor Henslow, Cambridge*
Postmark: Jan 24 1833
From: Dr and the Misses Darwin]

Shrewsbury 1 Feb. 1833

Doctor & Miss Darwins present their Compts to Professor
Henslow and beg to return a great many thanks for his kindness
in allowing them to see the enclosed letters—the one written
August 15th is ten days later than any they have received.—
Shrewsbury
February 1st. 1833

LETTER 25

[*The following letter from Charles's father, Robert, was written from
Shrewsbury on March 7, 1833, and may help to dispel the somewhat grim
father-figure image that has grown up around him. The money references
suggest that Charles's anxieties of over-spending were unfounded. Though
he was obviously a man of few written words, we should not forget that he
carried on a daily monologue of talk. There was a 'want of liberty at
Shrewsbury whenever Dr Darwin was in the room; but then he was genial
and sympathetic, only nobody must go on about their own talk'[1].*]

[*To: Charles Darwin Esq*ʳᵉ
From: Dr. R. W. Darwin]

[*Shrewsbury*]
7 March 1833

My dear Charles
As a packet of letters is going under cover to Capt Beaufort I
must send you one line, tho' in fact I have not any thing to say
besides expressing the pleasure we all feel at your still continuing
to enjoy health and your voyage. We all are very happy when we
get a letter from you.
In consequence of the recommendation in your first letter I got a
Banana tree, it flourishes so as to promise to fill the hot-house.

---

[1] Litchfield, H. E., ed., *Emma Darwin*, John Murray, 1915. Letter from Emma
Darwin to Julia Wedgwood, Vol. 1, p. 60.

I sit under it, and think of you in similar shade. You know I never write any thing besides answering questions about medicine and therefore as you are not a patient I must conclude.

Your money accounts are all correct. The L20 in November has appeared, the other for Capt Fitzroy I have not yet received.

My dear Charles ever your affectionate

R. W. Darwin

Salop
7 March 1833

LETTER 26

[*To: The Rev^d. Prof: Henslow Cambridge*
Postmark: L AU21 1833]

April 11th 1833

My dear Henslow

We are now running up from the Falkland Islands to the Rio Negro (or Colorado). The Beagle will proceed to M: Video; but if it can be managed I intend staying at the former place.—It is now some months since we have been at a civilized port, nearly all this time has been spent in the most Southern part of Tierra del Fuego.—It is a detestable place, gales succeed gales with such short intervals that it is difficult to do anything.—We were 23 days off Cape Horn & could by no means get to the Westward.—The last & finale gale, before we gave up the attempt was unusually severe. A sea stove [*altered from* staved] one of the boats & there was so much water on the decks, that every place was afloat; nearly all the paper for drying plants is spoiled & half of this cruizes collection.—We at last run in to harbor & in the boats got to the West by the inland channels.—As I was one of this party, I was very glad of it: with two boats we went about 300 miles, & thus I had an excellent opportunity of geologising & seeing much of the Savages.—The Fuegians are in a more miserable state of barbarism than I had expected ever to have seen a human being.—In this inclement country, they are absolutely naked, & their temporary houses are like what children make in summer, with boughs of trees.—I do not think any spectacle can be more interesting, than the first sight of Man in his primitive wildness.—It is an interest, which cannot well be imagined untill it is experienced. I shall never forget [the *del*] when entering Good Success Bay, the yell with which a party received us. They were seated on a rocky point, surrounded by the dark forest of beech; as they threw their arms wildly round their heads & their long hair streaming, they seemed the troubled spirits of another world. —The climate in some respects, is a curious mixture of severity & mildness: as far as regards the animal kingdom the former character prevails; I have in consequence, not added much to my collections.—The geology of this part of Tierra del was, as indeed every place is, to me very interesting.—the country is non-fossiliferous & a common place succession of granitic rocks & slates: attempting to make out the relation of cleavage, strata etc etc was my chief amusement.—The mineralogy however of some of the rocks, will I think be curious, from their resemblance to those of Volcanic origin.—In Zoology, during the whole cruize, I have done little; the Southern ocean is nearly as sterile as the continent it washes.—Crustaceae have afforded me most work: it is an order most imperfectly known: I found a Zoea, of most curious form, its body being only 1/6 the length of the two spears.—I am convinced from its structure & other reasons it is [9, B *added*][1] a young Erichthus!—I must mention part of the structure of a Decapod, it is so very anomalous: the last pair of legs are small & dorsal, but instead of being terminated by a claw, as in all others, it has three curved bristle-like appendages; these are finely serrated & furnished with cups, somewhat resembling those of the Cephalopods.—The animal being pelagic, it is a beautiful structure to enable it to hold on to light floating objects.—I have found out something about the propagation of that ambiguous tribe, the Corallines.[2]—And this makes up nearly the poor cata-

---

[1] The meaning of 9, B unexplained.

[2] His interest in Corallines should be noted—more than two years before he saw a true coral island. See Letters 34 and 48, pp. 91, 130; and also D. R. Stoddart, 'C. Darwin: *Coral Islands*', *Atoll Research Bull.* 88, Dec. 1962. I am much indebted to Dr Stoddart, who allows me to add his summary of

logue of rarities during this cruize. After leaving Tierra del we
sailed to the Falklands. I forgot to mention the fate of the
Fuegians[1] whom we took back to their country.—They had become entirely Europaean in their habits & wishes: so much so that
the younger one had forgotten his own language & their countrymen paid but very little attention to them.—We built houses for
them & planted gardens, but by the time we return again on our
passage round the Horn, I think it will be very doubtful how
much of their property will be left unstolen.—On our arrival at
the Falklands, everyone was much surprised to find the English
flag hoisted. This our new island, is but a desolate looking spot,
yet must eventually be of great importance to shipping.—I had
here the high good fortune, to find amongst most primitive looking rocks, a bed of micaceous sandstone, abounding with Terebratula & its subgenera & Entrochitus. As this is so remote a
locality from Europe I think the comparison of these impressions,
with those of the oldest fossiliferous rocks of Europe will be preeminently interesting. Of course there are only models & casts;
but many of these are very perfect. I hope sufficiently so to iden-
tify species.—As I consider myself your pupil, nothing gives me
more pleasure, than telling you my good luck.—I am very impatient to hear from you. When I am sea-sick & miserable, it is
one of my highest consolations, to picture the future, when we
again shall be pacing together the roads round Cambridge. That
day is a weary long way off; we have another cruize to make to
Tierra del next summer, & then our voyage round the world will
[*crossed on earlier sheets*] really commence. Capt FitzRoy has purchased a large Schooner of 170 tuns. In many respects it will be
a great advantage having a consort: perhaps it may somewhat

Darwin's views in the light of recent knowledge; see Appendix 4. See also Bibliography under *Geology of the Voyage.*
[1] Four native Fuegians had been brought back from Tierra del Fuego in 1830,
from the earlier expedition under Captain King. Three were now being repatriated, one having succumbed to small-pox in spite of four efforts at vac-
cination. The three, Jemmy Button, York Minster and Fuegia Basket, were
returning with a veneer of education, Christian morality and the use of tools.
Captain FitzRoy's hopes of a regenerated Fuegia were not fulfilled.

shorten our cruize: which I most cordially hope it may: I trust however that the Corall reefs & various animals of the Pacific may keep up my resolution.—Remember me most kindly to Mrs Henslow & all other friends; I am a true lover of Alma Mater, & all its inhabitants. Believe me my dear Henslow

Your affectionate & most obliged friend
Charles Darwin

Recollect, if [*you*] should think of any books, scientific travels etc etc which would be useful to me, do not let them pass out of y^r mind.

We are all very curious to [some great *del*] to hear *something* about *some* great Comet[1] which is coming at *some* time: Do pump the learned & send us a report.

I am convinced from talking to the finder, that the Megatherium, sent to Geol: Soc: belongs to same formation which those bones I sent home do & that it was washed into the River from the cliffs which compose the banks: Professor Sedgwick might like to know this: & tell him I have never ceased being thankful for that short tour in Wales.

LETTER 27

[To: The Rev^d. Prof: Henslow Cambridge
No postmark]

Rio de la Plata July 18th 1833
H.M.S. Beagle

My dear Henslow, My last letter was dated on the sea.—I then expected to stop at the R. Negro in Patagonia; our domineering master, the wind, ordered otherwise; in consequence the greater part of this winter has been passed in this river at Maldonado.— Amongst a heap of letters which awaited me, I was sadly disappointed not to see your hand-writing: for several months I had been looking forward with no little pleasure to hearing [all *del*] how you all are going on at Cambridge, & with a good deal of

[1] See Letter 28, p. 78.

anxiety respecting the fate of my collections.—Our direction, for a long period hence, will be Valparaiso: I should be so much obliged if you would write to me.—You only know anything about my collections, & I feel as if all future satisfaction after this voyage will depend solely upon your approval. I am afraid you have thought them very scanty; but, as I have said before, you must recollect how much time is lost at sea, & that I make it a constant rule to prefer the obscure & diminutive tribes of animals.—I have now got a servant of my own,[1] whom I have taught to skin birds etc, so that for the future I trust, there will be rather a larger proportion of showy specimens.—We have got almost every bird in this neighbourhead[2] (Maldonado), about 80 in number & nearly 20 quadrupeds.—But, alas, excepting this, there has not been much done.—By the same packet, which takes this there will come [*here a space must have been left for filling in the details of the cargo later, only achieved by smaller writing & compression*] four barrells: the largest will require opening, as it contains skins, Plants etc etc, & cigar box with pill boxes: the two next in size, only Geological specimens, need not be opened, without you like to see them, [*end of space*] the [two *del*] smallest & flat barrell contains fish; with a gimlet you can easily ascertain how full [they are *del*] it is of spirits.—Several of the pill-boxes are marked thus (X), they contain Coleoptera, & will require (as likewise the case) airing & perhaps a little Essential oil.—This is not nearly all which I have collected this summer, but for several reasons I have deferred sending the other half.—It is useless

[1] Syms Covington. In a letter to his sister Catherine, dated May 22, 1833, Darwin wrote: 'The following business piece is to my Father: having a servant of my own would be a really great addition to my comfort, for these two reasons; as at present, the Captain has appointed one of the men to be with me, but I do not think it just thus to take a seaman out of the ship; and 2nd when at sea, I am rather badly off for anyone to wait on me. The man is willing to be my servant, & ALL the expences would be under £60 per annum. I have taught him to shoot & skin birds, so that in my main object he is very useful.' (*See Charles Darwin and the Voyage of the 'Beagle'*, p. 85. Syms Covington, who started the voyage as 'Fiddler and Boy to the Poop Cabin', became Darwin's servant in the second year and remained in his service for several years after their return to England. See *Notes & Records of the Royal Society*, Vol. 14, No. 1, p. 12, by Sir Gavin de Beer.
[2] So spelt until the last months of the voyage.

attempting to thank you for taking charge of my collections: for as I know no other person who would; this voyage would then be useless & I would return home.—Our future plans are, in a few days to go to the R. Negro, to survey some banks.—I shall be put on shore: I wish we could remain there for a long time.—The geology must be very interesting—it is near the junction of the Megatherium & Patagonian cliffs.—From what I saw of the latter in one half hour in St Josephs bay, they would be well worth a long examination.—above the great Oyster bed, there is one of gravel, which fills up inequalities in its inferior; & above this, & therefore high out of the water is one of such modern shells, that they retain their colour & emit bad smell when burnt. Patagonia must clearly [have a very *del*] have but lately risen from the water. After the Beagle returns from this short cruize, we take in 12 months provisions & in beginning of October proceed to Tierra del F., then pass the Straits of Magellan & enter the glorious Pacific: The Beagle after proceeding to Conception or Valparaiso, will once more go Southward, (I however will not leave the warm weather) & upon her return we proceed up the coast, ultimately to cross the Pacific.—I am in great doubt whether to remain at Valparaiso or Conception: at the latter beds of Coal & shells, but at the former I could cross & recross the grand chain of the Andes.—I am ready to bound for joy at the thoughts of leaving this stupid, unpicturesque side of America. When Tierra del F is over, it will all be Holidays. And then the very thoughts of the fine Corals, the warm glowing weather, the blue sky of the Tropics is enough to make one wild with delight. —I am anxious to know, what has become of a large collection (I fancy ill assorted) of Geological specimens [made in former voyage *added*] from Tierra del Fuego.

I hope to see enough of this country to be able to make a rough sketch of it—& then of course specimens with localities marked on them, would be to me very valuable. Remember me most kindly to Prof. Sedgwick, perhaps he would enquire at Geol: Soc: whether they are in existence.—Somebody told me you had Volume of Dic Class: Explan: of Plates. My brother will in short time send me a parcel: by which it can come: his direction is Whyndham Club, St James Square. If you know of any book, which would be useful to me, you can mention it to him: I trust I shall find a letter (although it is a long time to look forward to) at Valparaiso; I shall be so glad to hear what you are doing.— Very often during your last Spring when the weather has been fine; I have been guessing whether it would do for Gamlingay or whether at that very instant some revered Botanist was not anxiously looking at the *other* side of a fenny ditch.—The only piece of Cambridge news which I have heard for a long time was a good one, it was that a Living has been given to you.—I hope it is true.—Remember me most truly to Mrs. Henslow & to Leonard Jennings.—Believe me My dear Henslow—Your most obliged & affectionate friend

Chas. Darwin

LETTER 28

[*To: C. Darwin*
From: Professor J. S. Henslow]

Cambridge 31 Augt 1833

My dear Darwin,

I am afraid that I have been rather negligent in not writing sooner to announce the arrival of your last Cargo which came safe to hand excepting a few articles in the Cask of Spirits which are spoiled, owing to the spirit having escaped thro' the bung-hole—I am now in possession of your letter of last April, which has stirred me up to send you off a few books which I thought might interest you, & I have (or rather *shall*) write to your Brother to recommend one or two more—The fossil portions of the Megatherium turned out to be extremely interesting as serving to illustrate certain parts of the animal which the specimens formerly received in this country & in France had failed to do— Buckland & Clift exhibited them at the Geological Section[1] (what

[1] Of the British Association's third meeting held in Cambridge under the presidency of Professor Adam Sedgwick. The meeting in 1832, the second after

this means you will learn from the report I send you)—& I have just received a letter from Clift requesting me to forward the whole to him, that he may pick them out carefully repair them, get them figured, & return them to me with a description of what they are & how far they serve to illustrate the osteology of the Great Beast—This I shall do in another week when I return again to Cambridge—for I am staying at present at Ely & am here merely on Saturday for L. Jenyn's duty tomorrow he having been unwell & advised not to take duty at present—I have popped the various animals that were in the Keg into fresh spirits in jars & placed them in my cellar—The more delicate things as insects, skins etc—I keep at my own house, with the precaution of putting Camphor into the bones—The plants delight me exceedingly, tho' I have not yet made them out—but with Hooker's work & help I hope to do so before long—I never thought of putting your name down to a Tablet we have been erecting to poor Ramsay's memory in Jesus Chapel till lately—As the list has not yet appeared I have ventured to do so for 21/– I propose having an engraving (I think I told you) from an excellent likeness which Miss Jenyn's made for me—& this I shall let the subscribers to the Tablet have at whatever the cost price may be, about 10/ or 12/– probably: I am sure from your respect for R's memory I have not done wrong in putting down your name—The comet you speak of is *expected* in 1835, according to calculation—but it seems very doubtful whether the calculation is correct—The papers of course talk nonsense about it, but it is really something out of the ordinary cometical occurrences[1]—Mrs Henslow produced me a fine girl on June 23, the day before the Association

the foundation in 1831, was presided over by the Rev. William Buckland, F.R.S., 1784–1880, writer on natural history subjects. For William Clift, see footnote 1, Letter 31, p. 83.

[1] 'The return of Halley's Comet again in 1835, and the extreme exactitude with which it conformed to its predicted course, is a testimony of truth, which must appear striking even to the most incurious respecting such matters.' Whewell's *History of the Inductive Sciences*, Vol. II, p.184, third edition, 1857. Halley, 1656–1742, predicted this recurrence from calculations on a periodicity of 75–6 years, dating back to the fourteenth century. The reappearance as predicted in 1835 was the seventh return of the comet.

met—It proved quite a breeding week with the Cambridge Ladies Mrs Clark[1] & Mrs Willis being confined within a day or two of the same time—I long as much as you do to see the day when we shall be discussing the various events of your voyage together, but I hope also that there is much yet to arrive before you bend your way home again. Not but what I w^d have you return immediately if you are really tired out—but you remember how we used to talk of the certainty of many an annoyance that must arrive, & many a wish to be home again—If you propose returning before the whole period of the voyage expires, don't make up your mind in a hurry—but let it be a steady thought for at least a month without one single desire to continue—& if such an event should occur you may fairly conclude that you are sick of the expedition but I suspect you will always find something to keep up your courage. Send home every scrap of Megatherium skull you can set your eyes upon—& *all* fossils. Use your sweeping net well for I forsee that your minute insects will nearly all turn out new—(I must write on now to the end as I have transgressed the limits)—I have turned Entomologist myself this summer for my little girls who have started on collections of Insects & Shells—& make me work for them—Poor Stephens has just lost 400£ in a Law suit & we are levying a subscription to help him on with his Illustrations—I delight in your descriptions of the few animals you now & then allude to—

Believe me
affect^y yrs
J. S. Henslow

[*This letter reached Darwin in March 1834 at the E. Falkland Islands (see Letter 31, p. 83).*]

[1] Wife of William Clark, 1788–1869, Professor of Anatomy, 1817–66. The son born in August 1833, was John Willis Clark, 1833–1910, who became Registrar of the University, and an important Cambridge figure. He collaborated with Robert Willis, husband of the above Mrs Willis, in the *Architectural History of the University and Colleges of Cambridge,* and wrote the *Concise Guide to Cambridge.* He also collaborated in the *Life of Professor Sedgwick,* 2 vols., 1890.

Robert Willis, 1800–75, was Professor of Mechanism, writer and archaeologist.

LETTER 29

[*To: The Revd Professor Henslow Cambridge University England
Specimens of Natural History:
No postmark*]

Buenos Ayres September 1833

My dear Henslow

A Spanish friend in Entre Rios has promised to send me a cargo of Bones; if they do arrive here, Mr Lumb has kindly offered to forward them to you.—

I leave this as a direction to him, & he will add the name of Ship, date, port etc or whatever is necessary.—

Believe me your most truly obliged

Charles Darwin

LETTER 30

[*To: The Revd Professor Henslow Cambridge
No postmark*]

Monte Video [Oct Sept *del*]
November 12th 1833

My dear Henslow.—

By the same packet, which takes this I send a cargo of specimens.—There are two boxes & a cask.—One of the former is lined with tin-plate & contains nearly 200 skins of birds & animals.—amongst others a fine collection of the mice of S. America.—the other box contains spirit bottles, & will only require just looking at to see how the Spirit stands.—But the Bird-skins, if you will take the trouble, will be much better for a little airing.—The Cask is divided into Compartments, the upper contains a few skins.—the other a jar of fish, & *I am very anxious to hear how the Spirit withstands evaporation,*—an insect case, which would require airing, a small box of stones, which may be left in statu quo,—a bundle of seeds,[1] which I send as a most humble apology for my idleness in Botany.—They were collected in Port

[1] See Appendix III, footnote, p. 232.

Alegra & in this country: the temperature of the former, must be
that of a warm greenhouse,—& even plants of this country would
require some protection (the olive & orange bear fruit here).—
Also a bag of the sweepings of a Granary; it will be a Botanical
problem to find out to what country the weeds belong: It might
be curious to observe whether Europaean weeds have undergone
any change by their residence in this country.[1]—If they are like
the men, I will answer for it they are not much improved.—I also
send to the care of Dr. Armstrong in Plymouth, an immense box
of Bones & Geological specimens. I do this to avoid the long land-
carriage: & as they do not want any care it does not much signify
where kept.—another reason is, not feeling quite sure of the value
of such bones as I before sent you.—I have one mutilated skeleton of the animal of which I sent the jaw with 4 small teeth.[2]

Since my last letter to you (middle of July, when I sent off some
specimens) I have been, as they say here, un grande golopeador.
—I left the Beagle at the R. Negro & crossed by land to B. Ayres.
There is now carrying on a bloody war of extermination against
the Indians, by which I was able to make this passage.—But at
the best it is sufficiently dangerous, & till now very rarely
travelled.—it is the most wild, dreary plain imaginable; without
[one *del*] settled inhabitant or head of cattle. There are military
Postas, at wide intervals, by which means I travelled.—We lived
for many days on deer & ostriches & had to sleep in the open
camp.—I am quite charmed with the Gaucho life: my luggage
consisted of a Hammer, Pistol & shirt & the Recado (*saddle*)
makes the bed: Where-ever the horses tire, there is your house &
home:—I had the satisfaction of ascending the Sierra de la Ventana, a chain of mountains between 3 & 4000 feet high, the very
existence of which is scarcely known beyond the Rio Plata.—
After resting a week at Buenos Ayres, I started for the St Fe; on
the road the Geology was interesting. I found two great groups

---

[1] Perhaps the first experimental interest in weeds and aliens.
[2] Here is added a small diagram and very faint writing.

of immense bones; but so very soft as to render it impossible to remove. I think from a fragment of one of the teeth they belonged to the Mastodon: In the R. Carcarana I got a tooth which puzzles even my conjectures, it looks like an enormous gnawing one.— At St. Fe, not being well, I embarked & had a fine sail of 300 miles down that princely river the Parana.—When I returned to B. Ayres I found the country upside down with revolutions, which caused me much trouble. I [at] last got away & joined the Beagle.—I am now going to have one more gallop to the Uruguay, & then we are off to Tierra del Fuego.—We shall for the future be much amongst Volcanic rocks, & I shall want more mineralogical knowledge.—Can you send me out any books, which with instructions from yourself, will enable me to use my reflecting Goniometers. If you know of any, it would [*be*] doing me a great favour to send it to Capt. Beaufort, who will forward it.—As I am very anxious to hear from you,—perhaps this will be the best manner of sending me a letter,—I want much to hear about your family—L. Jenyns, your lectures, excursions & parties etc.—respecting all of which I have so very many pleasant recollections, that I cannot bear to know nothing.—We shall pass the St^s of Magellan in the Autumn & I hope to stay some time in the southern parts of Chili. There are two Volcanoes within 60 miles of Conception. I will run the risk of being eat up alive to see two real good burning Volcanoes. Oh the blue skys & the Bananas of the Tropics.—Life is not worth having in these miserable climates, after one peep within those magic lines.—

Believe me my dear Henslow
Ever yours most truly obliged
Chas. Darwin.—

[*A postscript across the top of p. 1 of this letter reads:*]
Would it not be a good plan to send sea-weeds in Spirits having previously noted the colour by Werner??[1]

---

[1] Werner's *Nomenclature of Colours*, Edinburgh, 1821.

LETTER 31

[*To:The Rev^d. Professor Henslow Cambridge
No postmark*]

E. Falkland Isd. March 1834

My dear Henslow

Upon our arrival at this place I was delighted at receiving your letter dated Aug. 31 [*see Letter 28, p. 77*].—Nothing for a long time has given me so much pleasure. Independent of the pleasure, your account of the arrival of my second cargo & that some of the specimens were interesting, has been, as you may well suppose, most highly satisfactory to me.—I am quite astonished that such miserable fragments of the Megatherium should have been worth all the trouble Mr Clift[1] has bestowed on them. I have been alarmed at the expression cleaning all the bones, as I am afraid the [printed *added*] numbers will be lost: the reason I am so anxious they should not be, is that a part were found in a gravel with recent shells, but others in a very different bed;—how with these latter there were bones of an Agouti, a genus of animals I believe now peculiar to America, & it would be curious to prove some one of the same genus co-existed with the Megatherium; such & many other points *entirely* depend on the numbers being carefully preserved.—My entire ignorance of comparative Anatomy makes me quite dependent on the numbers: so that you will see my geological notes will be useless without I am certain to what specimens I refer.—Since receiving these specimens you ought to have received two other cargos, shipped from Plata in July & November 1833.—With the latter there was a heavy box of fossil remains, which is now I suppose at Plymouth. I followed this

[1] William Clift, 1775–1849, born at Bodmin; went as assistant to John Hunter in London in 1792, becoming Keeper of his Museum before Hunter's death in 1793. He was kept on at a miserable salary for six years, during which time he copied most of Hunter's MSS and cleaned the collection. The original MSS were destroyed by Sir Everard Home, perhaps because he recorded their contents in papers published under his own name. The Royal College of Surgeons was inaugurated when Hunter's Collection was purchased by the Corporation of Surgeons in 1799, Clift remaining as Keeper. His daughter married Richard Owen in 1835.

plan from not liking to give you so much trouble: it contains another imperfect Megatherium head, & some part of the skeleton of an animal, of which I formerly sent the jaw, which had four teeth on each side in shape ⊂⊃ ⊂⊃ o o like this.—I am anxious to know to what it belongs.—Shortly before I left M. Video I bought [far up in the country *added*] for two shillings a head of a Megatherium which must have been when found quite perfect.—The Gauchos however broke the teeth & lost the lower jaw, but the lower & internal parts are tolerably perfect: It is now, I hope, on the high seas in pursuit of me.—It is a most flattering encouragement to find men, like Mr. Clift, who will take such interest in what I send home.—I am very glad the plants give you any pleasure, I do assure you I was so ashamed of them, I had a great mind to throw them away; but if they give you any pleasure I am indeed bound, & will pledge myself to collect whenever we are in parts not often visited by Ships & Collectors.—I collected all the plants, which were in flower on the coast of Patagonia at Port Desire & St Julian; also on the Eastern parts of Tierra del Fuego, where the climate & features of T. del Fuego & Patagonia are united. With them are as many seeds, as I could find (you had better plant all the rubbish which I send, for some of the seeds are very small).—The soil of Patagonia is *very* dry, *gravelly* & light, —in East Tierra, it is gravelly—peaty & damp.—Since leaving the R. Plata, I have had some opportunities of examining the great Southern Patagonian formation.—I have a good many shells; from the little I know of the subject, it must be a Tertiary formation for some of the shells & (Corallines?) now exist in the sea.— & others I believe do not.—This [Patag *del*] bed, which is chiefly characterised by a great Oyster is covered by a very curious bed of Porphyry pebbles, which I have traced for more than 700 miles; but the most curious fact is that the whole of the East coast [of South part of S. America *added*] has been elevated from the ocean, since a period, during which Muscles have not lost their blue color.—At Port St Julian I found some very perfect bones of some large animal, I fancy a Mastodon.—the bones of one hind extremity [were *del*] are very perfect & solid.—This is interesting

as the Latitude is between 49° & 50° & the site is so far removed
from the great Pampas [plains *del*] where bones of the narrow
toothed Mastodon are so frequently found. By the way this
Mastodon & the Megatherium, I have no doubt, were fellow
brethren in the ancient plains. Relics of the Megatherium I have
found at a distance of nearly 600 miles apart in a N. & S. line.—
In Tierra del Fuego I have been interested in finding some sort of
[Nautilus *del*] Ammonite (also I believe found by Capt. King) in
the Slate near Port Famine; & on the Eastern coast there are some
curious alluvial plains, by which [*I del*] the existence of certain
quadrupeds in the islands can clearly be accounted for.—There
is a sandstone, with the impression of the [presen *del*] leaves like
the common Beech tree[1] also modern shells, etc etc.—On the
surface of which table land there are, as usual, muscles with their
blue color etc.—This is the *report* of my *geological* section! to
you my President & Master.—I am quite charmed with Geology
but like the wise animal between two bundles of hay, I do not
know which to like the best, the old crystalline group of rocks or
the softer & fossiliferous beds.—When puzzling about stratification etc, I feel inclined to cry a fig for your big oysters & your
bigger Megatheriums.—But then when digging out some fine
bones, I wonder how any man can tire his arms with hammering
granite.—By the way I have not one clear idea about cleavage,
stratification, lines of upheaval.—I have no books, which tell me
much & what they do I cannot apply to what I see. In consequence
I draw my own conclusions, & most gloriously ridiculous ones
they are, I sometimes fancy I shall persuade myself there are no
such things as mountains, which would be a very original discovery to make in Tierra del Fuego.—Can you throw any light
into my mind, by telling me what relation cleavage & planes of
deposition bear to each other?—And now for my second *section*
Zoology.—I have chiefly been employed in preparing myself for
the South sea, by examining the Polypi of the smaller Corallines

---

[1] Probably leaves of one of the species of *Nothofagus*, the analogue of *Fagus* in
the Southern Hemisphere. Several species are abundant in Tierra del Fuego,
especially *N. betuloides* (*Mirb.*) Oerst.—N. Y. S.

in these latitudes.—Many in themselves are very curious, & I think are quite undescribed, there was one appalling one, allied to a Flustra which I daresay I mentioned having found to the Northward, where the cells have a moveable organ (like a Vultures head, with a dilatable beak), fixed on the edge. But what is of more general interest is the unquestionable (as it appears to me) existence of another species of ostrich, besides the Struthio Rhea. All the Gauchos & Indians state it is the case: & I place the greatest faith in their observations.—I have the head, neck, piece of skin, feathers, & legs of one. The differences are chiefly in color of feathers, & scales on legs, being feathered below the knees; nidification & geographical distribution.—[1]

So much for what I have lately done; the prospect before me is full of sunshine: fine weather, glorious scenery, the geology of the Andes; plains abounding with organic remains, (which perhaps I may have the good luck to catch in the very act of moving); & lastly an ocean & its shores abounding with life.—So that, if nothing unforeseen happens I will stick to the voyage; although, for what I can see, this may last till we return a fine set of white-headed old gentlemen.—I have to thank you most cordially for sending me the Books.—I am now reading the Oxford Report.—[2] the whole account of your proceedings is most glorious; You, remaining in England, cannot well imagine how excessively interesting I find the reports; I am sure, from my own thrilling sensations, when reading them, that they cannot fail to have an excellent effect, upon all those residing in distant colonies, & who have little opportunity of seeing the Periodicals.—My hammer has flown with redoubled force on the devoted blocks; as I thought over the eloquence of the Cambridge President I hit harder & harder blows. I hope, to give my arm strength for the Cordilleras, you will send me, through Capt. Beaufort, a copy of the Cambridge Report.—

I have forgotten to mention, that for some time past & for the

[1] See *Ornithological Notes, Bull. B.M. (N.H.)*, Vol. 2, No. 7, 1963. Here Darwin gives his diagnoses of the differences in the two ostriches. The new species was named *Rhea darwinii* after he had exhibited the portions brought back with him on his return.   [2] British Association Meeting, 1832.

future, I will put a pencil cross on the pill-boxes containing insects, as these alone will require being kept particularly dry, it
may perhaps save you some trouble.—When this letter will go, I
do not know, as this little seat of discord has lately been embroiled
by a dreadful scene of murder & at present there are more
prisoners, than inhabitants.—If a merchant vessel is chartered to
take them [to Rio *added*] I will send some specimens (especially
my few plants & seeds).—Remember me to all my Cambridge
friends.—I love & treasure up every recollection of dear old
Cambridge.—I am much obliged to you for putting my name
down to poor Ramsay's monument—I never think of him without the warmest admiration.—Farewell my dear Henslow—
believe my [*me*] your most obliged & affectionate friend. Charles
Darwin.—N.B. What I have said about the numbers attached to
the fossils, applies to every part of my collections.—Videlicet.
Colors of all the Fish: habits of birds etc etc:

There is no opportunity of sending a cargo: I only send this,
with the seeds, some of which I hope may grow, & show the
nature of the plants far better than my Herbarium. They go
through Capt. Beaufort: give Mr Whewell[1] my best thanks for
sending me his tide paper: all on board are much interested by

[1] Rev. W. Whewell, 1794–1866, Master of Trinity College, Cambridge from
1841–66, had begun to take an interest in Charles Darwin as an undergraduate.
In his *Autobiography*, p. 66, Charles wrote: 'Dr Whewell was one of the older and
distinguished men who sometimes visited Henslow, and on several occasions I
walked home with him at night.' Although Charles cannot have read Whewell's
History of the Inductive Sciences until after his return from the *Beagle* voyage (the
first edition was published in 1837), he must have heard his discourse in a philosophical vein on science in a manner which may have influenced him profoundly,
seeking as he was for an open-minded approach. After his return, Charles praised
Whewell's *History of the Inductive Sciences* to Robert Brown, who was incapable
of appreciating him; Darwin could thus measure up their different scientific philo-
sophies. (See *Autobiography*, p. 104.) Whewell is also mentioned in Letter 47 of
May 1837 and in Letter 54, October 1837. In Letter 68, April 1848, Darwin
wrote to Henslow from Down, mentioning 'the anecdote about Whewell and the
Tides'—possibly referring to Whewell's work on tides, when he arrived at the
conclusion, from comparison of the observations made in 1836 in the German
Ocean, 'that there must be a point in the German Ocean, about midway between
Lowestoft . . . and the Dutch coast where the tide would vanish: and this was
ascertained to be the case by observation . . .' (See *History of the Inductive
Sciences*, 1837, p. 471.) Darwin had also received Whewell's Presidential Address
to the British Association, 1833.

it.—Remember me most kindly to Mrs. Henslow & Leonard
Jenyns.—

LETTER 32

[To: The Revd Professor Henslow Cambridge University
From: Edward Lumb of Buenos Ayres
No Postmark]

Bs. Ayres May 2^d 1834

Sir,

I beg to enclose your bill of lading for a Case of Specimens of
Natural History which by direction of Mr Charles Darwin I
forward to you p. Brig "Basenthwaite" Mitchinson Martin for
Liverpool = This Case contains part of the Head of the "Megatherium"—I regret that on the passage down the River it should
have been broken; previous to this accident the Snout or nose
extended $1\frac{1}{2}$ to two feet more than at present—These are not the
bones referred to in the accompanying Letter—I expect them
down shortly when I shall feel proud in forwarding them to you—
Permit me this opportunity of offering my Services to you & to
assure you that I shall feel highly gratified if by any Information,
or Specimens I can obtain in this Country I can contribute to the
advancement of Science in my native land—

My last letter from Mr. Darwin was from the Falkland Islands
30 March; at which time all was well—

I have the honour to be Sir
Your most ob^d Ser^t
Edward Lumb

LETTER 33

[*To: C. Darwin Esq. H.M.S. 'Beagle', Valparaiso, S. America.*
From: J. S. Henslow Paid 3/7
Postmark: Shrewsbury, Aug 5, 1834]

Cholsey, Wallingford,[1]
22 July 1834

My dear Darwin

It is now some months since I received your last letter with the intention of answering it so soon as I should be able to give you an account of the safe arrival of your cargo of skins etc. These were delayed at Dr Armstrongs up to the time of my quitting Cambridge & I have only just heard that he has at length despatched them. He tells me however that everything is safe, & that he had used the precaution of opening the cases & airing everything for you—I had recommended the fossils to be all sent to Mr Clift at Surgeon's Hall who has kindly undertaken to repair them & prepare them so that they shall be preserved without injury—Judging from what you sent before I did not hesitate to do this as they will be well worth the carriage to London, & could not possibly be in better hands than Clift's. I regret that I did not get the sweepings of the granary before I left Cambridge as I fear the delay will spoil most of the seeds which cannot now be sown before next Spring—Pray don't entirely neglect to dry plants— Those sent are *all* of the greatest interest—Send minute things, such [*as*] the little ranunculus,[2] & common weeds & grasses, not to the neglect of flowering shrubs of which you have sent some nice species of Berberry[3] etc.—I have not your letter bye me to answer your questions formally but I remember you enquired about a Goniometer. I would not advise you to bother yourself

---

[1] In 1832 Henslow was offered the living of Cholsey-cum-Moulsford in Berkshire at a value of £340 per annum. He lived with his parishioners during the Long Vacation, returning to his Cambridge duties for the rest of the year. See Letter 22, p. 65. It was not until 1837 that he moved to Hitcham in Suffolk.

[2] Probably *Ranunculus biternatus* Sm., which Darwin collected at Tierra del Fuego in 1833 (specimen in the Cambridge University Herbarium).—N. Y. S.

[3] Possibly *Berberis buxifolia* Lam., *B. empetrifolia* Lam. or *B. ilicifolia* Forst., all of which occur in Tierra del Fuego.—N. Y. S.

with one. It is an instrument of no use in the field, & of importance
only in the hands of an experienced mineralogist in his *closet*.
Phillip's book must be quite as much as you *need* for the detection
of the few ingredients which form rocks—any that you can't make
out you must describe conditionally & we will get you to rights
10 years hence when you return—Fox & his wife spent a day
with us at commencement—he tells me that you are very irate at
not having heard from me—which I don't exactly understand, as
I should have thought that you ought to have received two letters
at least from me by the time he heard from you—That I have not
written as often as I ought I will readily admit—for I never do
anything as I ought—but really & truly I have written & I trust
that you have had positive proof of it before now. I don't know
that I have much local news to tell you which is likely to be of any
interest—You will see by the papers that we have been in various
kinds of hot water, in which however I am happy to say that I
have escaped from scalding my own fingers, though I fear that
the result has caused a few burnings & cuttings among certain
Members of the University who ought to be above such evils.—
Your Master, I suppose you know, is married, & soon to be a
Papa if all prospers—My own family is 3♀–1♂ & if you delay your
return much longer & I am equally fortunate as I have hitherto
been you may be in time to stand Godfather to another—I am
at present rusticating for the Vacation at my living—& enjoy the
change from a town to a country life most exceedingly—There
are no immediate neighbours & I am not bothered by morning
visits—My parish abounds in poor, & small farmers who leave
every thing to the parson without attempting to assist him—
However I am quite satisfied with my visit, the only drawback
being the long distance which I have to bring my family—about
100 miles—I shall be very anxious as the time for your return
approaches to hear of you & look forward with the prospect of
great satisfaction to the confabs we shall have together—Captn.
W. Ramsay is about to start as Commander of a Steam frigate for
the W. Indies & if I had been a single or an independent man I
should certainly have joined him for a few months cruise—How

you would have stared to have seen me walking on the Quay at
Monte Video. With kindest remembrances from all my family &
most hearty good wishes from myself believe me ever
Your affectionate friend
J. S. Henslow

LETTER 34

[*To: The Rev^d. Professor Henslow, Cambridge*
No postmark]
Valparaiso July 24th. 1834
My dear Henslow

   A box has just arrived, in which were two of your most kind
& affectionate letters; you do not know how happy they have
made me.—One is dated Dec. 12th. 1833 the other Jan: 15th. of
the *same year*![1] By what fatality it did not arrive sooner, I cannot
conjecture: I regret it much; for it contains the information I most
wanted about manner of packing etc etc: roots, with specimens of
plants etc etc: this [I suppose *added*] was written after the reception
of first cargo of specimens.—Not having heard from you untill
March of this year; I really began to think my collections were so
poor, that you were puzzled what to say: the case is now quite on
the opposite tack; for you are *guilty* of exciting all my vain feelings
to a most comfortable pitch; if hard work will atone for these
thoughts I vow it shall not be spared.—It is rather late, but I will
allude to some remarks in the Jan: letter: you advise me to send
home duplicates of my notes; I have been aware of the advantage
of doing so; but then at sea to this day, I am invariably sick, excepting on the finest of days; which [*altered to* at which times] with
pelagic animals around me, I could never bring myself to the task;
on shore the most prudent person, could hardly expect such a
sacrifice of time.—My notes are becoming bulky; I have about
600 small quarto pages full; about half of this is Geology, the
other imperfect descriptions of animals: with the latter I make it a
rule only to [note *del*] describe those parts which cannot be seen,
in specimens in spirits. I keep my private Journal distinct from
[1] See Letter 22 wrongly dated.

the above.[1]—(N.B. this letter is a most untidy one, but my mind is untidy with joy: it is your *fault*, so you must take the consequence). With respect to the land Planariae: unquestionably they are not Molluscous animals: I read your letter last night, this morning I took a little walk: by a curious coincidence I found a new white species of Planaria & a [new to me *added*] Vaginulus (3rd species which I have found in S. America) of Cuv: I suppose this is the animal Leonard Jenyns alludes to.—the *true Onchidium* of *Cuv*: I likewise know.—Amongst marine Mollusques I have seen a good many genera & at Rio found one quite new one.— With respect to the December letter, I am very glad to hear, the four casks arrived safe; since which time you will have received another cargo, with the bird skins about which [we were doubt *del*] you did not understand me.—Have any of the B. Ayrean seeds produced plants?—From the Falklands, I acknowledge a box & letter from you; with the letter were a few seeds from Patagonia.—At present I have specimens enough to make a heavy cargo, but shall wait as much longer as possible, because opportunities are not so good now as before.—I have just got scent of some fossil bones of a MAMMOTH! what they may be, I do not know, but if gold or galloping will get them, they shall be mine. You tell me, you like hearing how I am going on & what doing; & you well may imagine how much I enjoy speaking to anyone upon subjects, which I am always thinking about, but never have anyone to talk to with.—After leaving the Falklands, we proceeded to the R.S. Cruz; followed up the river till within 20 miles of the Cordilleras: Unfortunately want of provisions compelled us to return.[2] This expedition was most important to

This record of method in writing up his notes will be of importance when items 29–38 C.U.L. have all been investigated. It shows that the 'small quarto pages' were filled with his observations as soon after acquiring the specimens as was possible. See *Ornithological Notes*, *Bull B.M.* (*N.H.*), Vol. 2, No. 7.

[2] An account of the expedition was read at the meeting of the Royal Geographical Society in May, 1837, by Captain FitzRoy, two years before the official publication of the record of the Voyage. See *D*, pp. 221, 437. The party must have been within a few miles of discovering Lake Argentino, which connects with the other great Andean lakes, Viedma and San Martin. J. H. Gardiner reached the lake in 1837, see *Bol. d. Instituto Geogr. Argentino*, Vol. I, pp. 29–35. It was visited again by Dr Moreno in 1878.

me, as it was a transverse section of the great Patagonian formation.—I conjecture (an accurate examination of fossils may possibly determine the point) that the main bed is somewhere about
the Miocene period (using Mr. Lyell's expression) I judge from
what I have seen of the present shells of Patagonia.—This bed
contains an enormous [mass *del*] field of Lava.—This is of some
interest, as being a rude approximation to the age of the Volcanic
part of the great range of the Andes.—Long before this it existed
as a Slate or *Porphyritic* line of hills.—I have collected tolerable
quantity of information respecting the period, (even numbers) &
forms of elevations of these plains. I think these will be interesting
to Mr. Lyell.[1]—I had deferred reading his third volume till my
return, you may guess how much pleasure it gave me; some of his
woodcuts came so exactly into play, that I have only to refer to
them, instead of re-drawing similar ones.—I had my Barometer
with me; I only wish I had used it more in these plains.—The
valley of S. Cruz appears to me a very curious one, at first it quite
baffled me.—I believe I can show good reasons for supposing it
to have been once a Northern St[ts]. [like that *added*] of *Magellan*.
—When I return to England, you will have some hard work in
winnowing my Geology; what little I know, I have learnt in such
a curious fashion, that I often feel very doubtful about the number
of grains: Whatever number they may turn out, I have enjoyed
extreme pleasure in collecting them.—In T. del Fuego I collected
& examined some Corallines:[2] I have observed one fact which
quite startled me.—it is, that in the genus Sertularia, (taken in its
most restricted form as by Lamouroux) & in 2 species which,
excluding comparative expressions, I should find much difficulty
in describing as different.—the Polypi quite & essentially differed;
in [all *added*] their most important & evident parts of structure.—

[1] Lyell's *Principles of Geology*, Vol. III, reached him in Valparaiso in 1834, Vol.
II he had received in Monte Video in 1832, and Vol. I he took with him, with
'given me by Capt. F. R. C. Darwin' in Darwin's own handwriting. All three
volumes are now in the Cambridge University Library. See Dr Sydney Smith on
'The Origin of "The Origin" ', *Advancement of Science*, No. 64, Brit. Assoc.
March 1960.
[2] See 'C. Darwin: *Coral Islands*', with an introduction by D. R. Stoddart, *Atoll
Research Bulletin* 88.

I have already seen enough to be convinced that the present families of Corallines, as arranged by Lamarck, Cuvier etc are highly artificial.—It appears they are in the same state which shells were when Linnaeus left them for Cuvier to rearrange.—I do so wish I was a better hand at dissecting: I find I can do very little in the minute parts of structure; I am forced to take a very rough examination as a type for different classes of structure.—It is most extraordinary I can no where see [in my books *added*] one single description of the polypus of any one Corall (excepting Lobularia [alcyonium *added*] of Savigny). I found a curious little stony Cellaria (a new genus) each cell provided with long toothed bristle, these are capable of various & rapid motions,—this motion is often simultaneous & can be produced by irritation.—this fact, as far as I see, is quite isolated in the history (excepting by the Flustra) with organ like Vultures Head [& an Escana *del*] of Zoophites—it points out a much more intimate relation between the Polypi, than Lamarck is willing to allow.—I forget, whether I mentioned, having seen something of the manner of propagation in that most ambiguous family, the Corallines: I feel pretty well convinced if they are not Plants, they are not Zoophites: the "gemmule".[1] of a Halimeda contained several articulations united & ready to burst their envelope & become attached to some basis. —I believe in Zoophites, universally the gemmule produces a single Polypus, which afterwards or at the same time, grows with its cell or single articulation.—The Beagle left the St^s of Magellan in the middle of winter; she found her road out by a wild unfrequented channel; well might Sir J. Narborough call the West coast South Desolation "because it is so desolate a land to behold". —We were driven into Chiloe[2] by some very bad weather;— An Englishman gave me 3 specimens of that very fine Lucanoidal insect, which is described Camb: Phil: Trans: 2 males & one female.—I find Chiloe is composed of Lava & recent deposits,— the Lavas are curious from abounding or rather being in parts

---

[1] A large square bracket and 17B is added above 'gemmule'.

[2] Darwin rode across the island of Chiloe, and wrote: 'The most singular result of the observations is that Chiloe is made 30 miles too long, hence it will be necessary to shorten the island ¼ of its received size.' See *D*, p. 257.

composed of Pitchstone.—If we go to Chiloe in the Summer I shall reap an Entomological harvest.—I [believe *del*] suppose the Botany both there & in Chili is well known.[1]—I forgot to state, that in the four cargoes of specimens there have been sent 3 square boxes, each containing four glass bottles.—I mention this in case they should be stowed beneath geological specimens, & thus escape your notice; perhaps some spirit may be wanted in them.— If a box arrives from B. Ayres. with Megatherium head & other *unnumbered* specimens: be kind enough to tell me; I have strong fears for its safety.—

We arrived here the day before yesterday; the views of the distant mountains are most sublime & the climate delightful; after our long cruize in the damp gloomy climates of the South, to breathe a clean, dry air, & feel honest warm sunshine, & eat good fresh roast beef must be the summum bonum of human life.—I do not like the looks of the rocks, half so much as the beef, there is too much of those rather insipid ingredients mica, quartz & Feldspar. —Our plans are at present undecided.—there is a good deal of work to the South of Valparaiso, & to the North an indefinite quantity.—I look forward to every part with interest. I have sent you in this letter a sad dose of egotism—but recollect I look up to you as my father in Natural History, & a son may talk about himself, to his father.—In your paternal capacity, as pro-proctor, what a great deal of trouble you appear to have had.—How turbulent Cambridge is become—Before this time it will have regained its tranquillity—I have a most schoolboy like wish to be there, enjoying my Holydays.—It is a most comfortable reflection to me, that a ship being made of wood & iron, cannot last for ever & therefore this voyage must have an end. October 28th:— This letter has been lying in my port-folio ever since July: I did not send it away, because I did not think it worth the postage: it shall now go with a box of specimens: shortly after arriving here, I set out on a geological excursion, & had a very pleasant ramble about the base of the Andes.—The whole country appears

---

[1] On Chiloe Darwin collected the *Berberis* which was described by Sir Wm. Hooker as *B. darwinii,* now well known in cultivation.—N. Y. S.

composed of breccias, (& I imagine Slates) which universally have
been modified, & oftentimes completely altered by the action of
fire; the varieties of porphyry thus produced is endless, but no
where have I yet met with rocks which have flowed in a stream;
dykes of [greenstone *added*] are very numerous: Modern Volcanic
action is entirely shut up in the very central parts (which cannot
now be reached on account of the snow) of the Cordilleras.—To
the South of the R. Maypo I examined the Tertiary plains, already
partially described by M. Gay.[1] The fossil shells appear to me, to
be far more different from the recent ones, than in the great
Patagonian formation: it will be curious if an Eocene & Meiocene
(Recent there is abundance of) could be proved to exist in
S. America as well as in Europe.—I have been much interested by
finding abundance of recent shells at an elevation of 1300 feet; the
country in many places is scattered over with shells, but these are
all littoral ones. So that I suppose the 1300 feet elevation *must* be
owing to a succession of small elevations such as in 1822. With
these certain proofs of the recent residence of the ocean over all
the lower parts of Chili, the outline of every view & the form of
each valley possesses a high interest. Has the action of running
water or the sea formed this deep ravine? Was a question which
often arose in my mind, & generally was answered by finding a
bed of recent shells at the bottom.—I have not sufficient arguments, but I do not believe that more than a small fraction of the
height of the Andes has been formed within the Tertiary period.—
The conclusion of my excursion was very unfortunate, I became
unwell & could hardly reach this place, I have been in bed for
the last month, but am now rapidly getting well.[2] I had hoped

[1] Monsieur Claude Gay, French naturalist, penetrated the Andes some years
before Darwin, and M. Brogniart reported on his work in *Annales des Sciences
Naturelles*, 1833. See Darwin's *Geological Observations*, 1876, pp. 293, 297. Also
mentioned in next letter. M. Gay seems to have contributed to the local papers on
the Viviparous lizard. (See Letter 38, p. 107.)

Author of *Historia Física y política de Chile: Botánica* (a flora of Chile in 8
vols., 1845–1852).—N. Y. S.

[2] This is the serious illness of Sept. 20 to the end of Oct. 1834, often referred
to in discussions of Darwin's later ill health. In *D*, p. 249, he states that 'Capt.
FitzRoy very kindly delayed the sailing of the ship till the 10th of November, by

during this time to have made a good collection of insects etc but it has been impossible. I regret the less, because Chili fairly swarms with Collectors; there are more Naturalists in the country, than Carpenters or Shoemakers or any other honest trade.—In my letter from the Falkland Is^d. I said I had fears about a box with a Megatherium. I have since heard from B. Ayres, that it went to Liverpool by the Brig Basingwaithe—If you have not received it,—it is, I think, worth taking some trouble about. In [September *del*] October two casks & a jar were sent by H.M.S. Samarang via Portsmouth. I have no doubt you have received them. With this letter I send a good many bird skins; in the same box with them, there is a paper parcel, containing pill-boxes with insects: the other pill-boxes require no particular care: you will see in two of these boxes, some dried Planariae, [terrestrial *added*] the only method I have found of preserving them (they are exceedingly brittle). By examining the white species I understand some little of the internal structure.—There are two small parcels of seeds.—There are some plants, which I hope may interest you, or at least those from Patagonia, where I collected everyone in flower:—there is a bottle, clumsily, but I think securely corked, containing water and *gaz* from the hot [Springs *del*] Baths of Cauquenes, seated at foot of Andes & long celebrated for medicinal properties.—I took pains in filling & securing both water & gaz,—If you can find any one who likes to analyze them; I should think it would be worth the trouble.—I have not time at present to copy my few observations about the locality etc etc of these Springs.—Will you tell me, how the Arachnidae, which I have sent home, for instance those from Rio, appear to be

---

which time I was quite well again.' The occasion when he describes the attack of the Big Black bug of the Pampas, the vector of Chagas disease, was not until March 1835, which does not preclude earlier attacks, from which he may possibly have contracted Chagas disease. See Professor S. Adler, O.B.E., F.R.S., *Nature*, Vol. 184, Oct. 10, 1959. Darwin stayed in the house of R. Corfield, referred to at the end of Letter 36, p. 99, an old Shrewsbury school friend, who was living in Valparaiso. He stayed there again in 1835, and wrote to his sister Susan: 'I have found him as kind & good-natured a friend as he is a good man . . . Do mention to Mr. Corfield of Pitchford, under what obligations I lie to his son.'

preserved.—I have doubts whether it is worth while collecting them.—

We sail the day after tomorrow: our plans are at last limited & definite: I am delighted to say we have bid an eternal adieu to T. del Fuego.—The Beagle will not proceed further South than C. Tres Montes. From which point we survey to the North. The Chonos archipelago is delightfully unknown; fine deep inlets running into the Cordilleras, where we can steer [sail *del*] by the light of a Volcano.—I do not know, which part of the voyage, offers the most attractions.—This is a shamefully untidy letter, but you must forgive me & believe me

My dear Henslow
Yours most truly obliged
Charles Darwin

Nov^r: 7th

LETTER 35[1]

[*To: Rev^d. Prof. Henslow Cambridge*]

October 4th, 1834. Valparaiso

My dear Henslow

I have been unwell & am not yet out of bed. I write to tell you that Capt. FitzRoy sent, a week ago, by H.M.S. Samarang through Portsmouth.—2 Casks, containing bones & stones & a box with 6 small bottles, with very valuable specimens.—Besides these two Casks there is a large Jar.—

I will write soon again when I am well. Dear Henslow

Yours affectionately
Chas Darwin

Valparaiso

---

[1] Letter 35 was written before Letter 34 was completed.

LETTER 36

[*To: The Rev^d. Professor Henslow Cambridge*]

Beagle. November 8th 1834
Valparaiso

My dear Henslow.—

This letter is merely to inform you that I send by H.M.S. Challenger two boxes with Specimens.—She does not sail from this port till January, & will not arrive in England for at least 4 months afterwards. This letter goes by the Challenger to England. —In one of the Cases, I have given you an account of all our proceedings & future prospects etc etc.—I have also sent a part of my Journal.—Would you be kind enough to direct and book it by some Coach to Dr Darwin Shrewsbury.—I did not think of sending it till five minutes before closing the Box, otherwise I would have directed it.—Of course if you are inclined, you can look at any part of my hum-drum letter-like journal. There are three small parcels of seeds; the one in the oblong box I have labelled as coming from T. del Fuego. it comes from Chiloe: (Climate etc etc like T. del Fuego but considerably warmer).—I do not much expect, that any one seed will grow.—

Continue to direct to Valparaiso: if you know any person in Liverpool who would put your letters to me by any of the numerous ships to this port I should receive them a couple of months sooner.—in this case they must be directed *to the care of R. Corfield Esqr*.

Yours most truly obliged   ·
Chas Darwin

LETTER 37

[*To: Professor Henslow Cambridge*
Postmark: M JY 15 1835 (therefore 4 months in transit)]

March 1835 [*Valparaiso*]

My dear Henslow

We now are lying becalmed off Valparaiso, & I will take the opportunity of writing a few lines to you. The termination of our voyage is at last decided on—we leave the coast of America in the beginning of [December *del*] September & hope to reach England in the same month of 1836.—I am heartily glad of it, nothing should induce me to stay out any longer. As it is, it will be nearly as long as a seven years transportation. But now that I do clearly see England in the distance, I care for nothing, not even sea sickness. In October perhaps I shall be in Cambridge & who knows but taking a walk with you round by Shelford common.— You can hardly understand how I long to see you & all my friends again; & now there only wants a year & half to that time. We shall see a great many places in this interval, but I am afraid there will be but little opportunities for Natural History. We are now making a passage from Concepcion.—You will have heard an account of the dreadful earthquake of the 20th of February. I wish some of the Geologists who think the Earthquakes of their times are trifling could see the way the solid rock is shivered. In the town there is not one house habitable; the ruins remind me of the drawings of the desolated Eastern cities.—We were at Baldivia at the time & felt the shock very severely. The sensation is more like that of skating over very thin ice; that is, distinct undulations were perceptible. The whole scene of Concepcion & Talcuana is one of the most interesting spectacles we have beheld since leaving England.—Since leaving Valparaiso, during this cruize, I have done little excepting in Geology.—In the modern Tertiary strata, I have examined 4 bands of disturbance, which reminded me on a small scale of the famous tract in the Isle of Wight.—In one spot there were beautiful examples of 3 different forms of upheaval.—In two cases I think I can show, that the inclination is owing to the presence of a system of parallel dykes traversing the inferior Mica Slate. The whole of the coast from Chiloe to S. extreme of the Pen: of Tres Montes is composed of the latter rock; it is traversed by very numerous dykes, the mineralogical nature of which will I suspect turn out very curious. I examined one grand transverse chain of Granite, which has clearly burst up through the overlying Slate. At P. Tres Montes there [is *del*] has been an old Volcanic focus, which corresponds to another in the North part of Chiloe. I was much pleased at Chiloe by finding a thick bed of [recent *added*] Oysters shells, etc, capping the Tertiary plain, out of which grew large forest trees.—I can now prove that both sides of the Andes have risen in the recent period, to a considerable height.—Here the shells were 350 ft above the sea.—In Zoology I have done but very little; excepting a large collection of minute Diptera & Hymenoptera from Chiloe. I took in one day, Pselaphus, Anaspis, Latridius, Leiodes, Cercyon & Elmis & two beautiful true Carabi; I might almost have fancied myself collecting in England. A new & pretty genus of Nudibranch Mollusc: which cannot crawl on a flat surface: & a genus in the family of Balanidae, which has not a true case, but lives in minute cavities of the shells of the Concholopas, are nearly the only two novelties. You were surprised at hearing of land Planariae; you will equally be so, when you see leaches, which live entirely out of water in the forests of Chiloe & Valdivia.—Before the Beagle sails for Lima, I shall be obliged to send away one more box: this will be the last, with which I shall trouble you. I am afraid so many boxes must have been very much in your way. I trust they may turn out worth their stowage. I will write again, when this last Cargo is sent. You ought to have received about a month since 2 boxes by H.M.S. Challenger & before that 2 Casks & one jar by H.M.S. Samarang.—Will you write to me directed to Sydney, not long after receiving this letter. —I am very unreasonable in begging for so many letters; but bear with me for one year more.—If any come directed [in the mean time *added*] to S. America, they will be forwarded to Sydney by the Admiral.—Valparaiso March 13th.—I am on the point of

starting to endeavour to pass the Cordilleras, but am very doubtful of the issue. Three month's letters are somewhere mislaid: but
I hope they will be found.—Perhaps there may be a letter from
you.—I am anxious to know whether the bird skins from the
River Plate in a tin box came safe.—I think that collection will be
good, as I took much pains with them.—I am in a great hurry, so
excuse this stupid, shabby little letter. Oh the goodly month of
September 1836.—To think I shall again be actually living quietly
in Cambridge.—It is too good a prospect, it will spoil the Cordilleras. So my dear Henslow good night

Your most obliged & affectionate friend

Chas. Darwin

LETTER 38

[*To: Professor Henslow Cambridge*
Postmark: M JY 15 1835[1]]

April 18th—1835
Valparaiso

My dear Henslow.—

I have just returned from Mendoza, having crossed the Cordilleras by two passes. This trip has added much to my knowledge of the geology of the country. Some of the facts, of [the
truth of *added*] which I in my own mind feel fully convinced, will
[(I fear) *added*] appear to you quite absurd & incredible.—I will
give a very short sketch of the structure of these huge mountains.
In the Portillo pass (the more Southern one) travellers have described the Cordilleras to consist of a double chain of nearly equal
altitude, separated by a considerable interval.—This is the case: &
the same structure extends to the Northward to Uspallata; the
little elevation of the Eastern line (here not more than 6,000–7,000
ft), has caused it almost to be overlooked. To begin with the
Western & principal chain; we have where the sections are best
seen, an enormous mass of Porphyritic conglomerate resting on

[1] This letter had therefore taken three months to reach England from Valparaiso.

Granite. This latter rock, seems to form the nucleus of the whole mass & is seen in the deep lateral valleys, injected amongst, upheaving, overturning in the most extraordinary manner the overlying strata. On the bare sides of the mountains, the complicated dykes & wedges of variously coloured rocks are seen traversing in every possible form & shape the same formations, which by their intersections prove a succession of violences. The stratification in all the mountains is beautifully distinct & from a variety in the color can be seen at great distances. I cannot imagine any part of the world presenting a more extraordinary scene of the breaking up of the crust of the globe than the very central peaks of the Andes. The upheaval [has taken place by *added*] by a great number of (nearly) N & S lines; which in most cases has formed as many anticlinal & synclinal ravines: The strata in the highest pinnacles are almost universally inclined at an angle from 70°–80°. —I cannot tell you how I enjoyed some of these views.—it is worth coming from England once to feel such intense delight. At an elevation from 10–12000 ft. there is a transparency in the air & a confusion of distances & a sort of stillness which gives the sensation of being in another world; & when to this is joined, the picture so plainly drawn of the great epochs of violence, it causes in the mind a most strange assemblage of ideas. The formation I call Porph—Conglomerates, is the most important & most developed one in Chili; from a great number of sections, I find it a true coarse Conglomerate or Breccia, which by every step in a slow gradation passes into a fine Clay-stone Porphyry; the pebbles & cement becoming Porphyrytic, till at last all is blended in one compact rock. The Porphyries are excessively abundant in this chain, I feel sure at least four of them have been thus produced from sedimentary beds in situ.—There are Porphyries which have been *in*jected from below [amongst strata *added*] & others [ejected *added*] which have flowed in streams: it is remarkable. I could show specimens of this rock, produced in these three methods, *which cannot be distinguished*. It is a great mistake considering the Cordilleras [(here) *added*] as composed of rocks which have flowed in streams: in THIS range I *no* where saw a fragment, which I believe to have thus originated, although the road passes at no great distance from the active Volcanoes.—The Porphyries, Conglomerates, Sandstones & Quartzose Sandstones, [Limestones *added*], alternate & pass into each other many times (overlying where not broken through by the Granite, Clay-Slate). In the upper parts, the Sandstone begins to alternate with Gypsum, till at last we have this substance of a stupendous thickness. I really think the formation is in some places (it varies much) nearly 2000 ft thick: it occurs often with a green (Epidote?) siliceous Sandstone & snow white marble: it resembles that found in the Alps in containing large concretions of a crystalline marble of a blackish grey color.—The upper beds, which form some of the higher pinnacles consist of layers of snow white gypsum & red compact sandstone, from the thickness of paper to a few feet, alternating in an endless round.—The rock has a most curiously painted appearance.—At the pass of the Puquenas in this formation, where however a black rock, like Clay-Slate, without many laminae occurring with a pale Limestone has replaced the red Sandstone I found abundant impressions of shells.—The elevation must be between 12–13000 ft.—A shell which I believe is a Gryphaea is the most abundant;—an Ostraea, Turritella, Ammonites, small Bivalves, Terebratula (?).—*Perhaps* some good Conchologist will be able to give a guess, to what grand division of the formations of Europe, these organic remains bear most resemblance.—They are exceedingly imperfect [& few *added*]. The Gryphites are most perfect.—It was *late* in the Season, & the situation particularly dangerous for snow storms. I did not dare to delay, otherwise a grand harvest might have been reaped.—So much for the Western line; in the Portillo pass, proceeding Eastward we meet an immense mass of a Conglomerate dipping to the West 45°, which rests on Micaceous Sandstones etc etc, upheaved, converted into quartz rock, penetrated by dykes, from the very grand mass of *Protogine* (large crystals of quartz, red Feldspar & occasional little Chlorite). Now this Conglomerate, which reposes on & dips from the Protogine ∠ 45°, consists of the peculiar rocks of the [above *del*] first described chain, [pebbles of *added*] the black

rock *with shells*, green sandstone etc etc: It is hence manifest that
the *upheaval* [(& deposition at least of part) *added*] of the Grand
Eastern chain is entirely posterior to the Western. To the North in
the Uspallata [pass *added*] we have also a fact of the same class.—
Bear this in mind, it will help to make you believe what follows.—
I have said the Uspallata range is geologically, although only
6000–7000 ft a continuation of the grand Eastern chain.—It has its
nucleus of granite, consists of grand beds of various crystalline
rocks, which I can feel no doubt are subaqueous lavas alternating
with Sandstone, Conglomerates, & white Aluminous beds (like
decomposed feldspar) with many other curious varieties of sedimentary deposits. These Lavas & Sandstones *alternate* very many
times & are quite conformable one to another. During two days of
careful examination I said to myself at least 50 times: how exactly
like, only rather harder, these beds are to those of the [upper *added*]
Tertiary strata of Patagonia, Chiloe, Concepcion, without the
possible identity *ever* having occurred to me.—At last there was
no resisting the conclusion.—I could not expect shells for they
never occur in this formation; but Lignite or Carbonaceous shale
[might *del*] ought to be found. I had previously been exceedingly
puzzled by meeting in the Sandstone, thin layers (few inches to
feet thick) of a brecciated Pitchstone.—I strongly suspect the
alteration, from the underlying Granite, has altered such beds into
this Pitchstone. The silicified wood, [(particularly characteristic)
added] was yet absent; the conviction that I was on the Tertiary
Strata was so strong, by this time in my mind, that on the third
day, in the midst of Lavas, & heaps of Granite I began my
apparently forlorn hunt.—How do you think I succeeded? In an
escarpement of compact greenish Sandstone I found a small wood
of petrified trees in a vertical position, or rather the strata were
inclined about 20[°]–30[°] to one point & the trees 70° to the opposite one.—That is they were before the tilt truly vertical.—The
Sandstone consists of *many* layers & is marked by the concentric
lines of the bark (I have specimens) 11 are perfectly silicified, &
resemble the dicotyledenous wood which I have found at Chiloe
& Concepciòn: the others [30–40 *added*] I only know to be trees

from the analogy of form & position; they consist of snow white columns, [Like Lots wife *added*] of coarsely crystall. Carb. of Lime. The longest shaft is 7 feet. They are all close together within a 100 yds & about same level; no where else could I find any.—It cannot be doubted that the *layers* of fine Sandstone have quietly been deposited between a clump of trees, which were fixed by their roots.—The Sandstone rests on Lavas, is covered by [*a*] great bed, apparently about 1000 ft thick, of black Augitic Lava, & over this, there are at least 5 grand alternations of such rocks & aqueous sedimentary deposits; amounting in thickness to several thousand feet.—I am quite afraid of the only conclusion which I can draw from this fact; namely that there must have been a depression in the surface of the land to that amount.—But neglecting this consideration it was a most satisfactory support of my presumption of the Tertiary (I mean by Tertiary, that the shells of the period were closely allied or some identical to those which now live as in lower beds of Patagonia) age of this Eastern Chain. A great part of the proof must remain upon my ipse dixit, of a mineralogical resemblance with those beds whose age is known, & the character of which resemblance, is to be subject to infinite variation, passing from one variety to others by a concretionary structure. I hardly expect you to believe me, when it is a consequence of this view that Granite which forms peaks of a height probably of 14000 ft has been fluid in the Tertiary period; —that strata of that period are altered by its heat & are traversed by *dykes* from the mass: that these Strata have also probably undergone an immense depression, that they are now inclined at high angles & form regular & complicated anticlinal lines.—To complete the climax & seal your disbelief these same sedimentary Strata & Lavas are traversed by very numerous true metallic veins of Iron, Copper, Arsenic, Silver & Gold, & that these can be traced to the underlying Granite.—A Gold mine has been worked close to the clump of silicified trees.—

If when you see my specimens, sections & account, you should think that there is pretty strong presumptive evidence of the above facts: It appears very important; for the structure, & size of this chain will bear comparison with any in the world. And [that *added*] this all should have been produced in so very recent a period is indeed wonderful. In my own mind I am quite convinced of the reality of this. I can anyhow most conscientiously say, that no previously formed conjecture warped my judgement. As I have described, so did I actually observe the facts.—But I will have some mercy & end this most lengthy account of my geological trip.—On some of the large patches of perpetual snow I found the famous Red Snow of the Arctic countries. I send with this letter my observations & a piece of Paper, on which I tried to dry some specimens. If the fact is new & you think it worth while, either yourself examine them or send them to whoever has described the specimens from the North, & publish a notice in any of the periodicals.—I also send a bottle with 2 Lizards: one of them is Viviperous, as you will see by the accompanying notice —A M. Gay,[1] a French Naturalist has already published in one of the Newspapers of this country a similar statement, & probably has forwarded to Paris some account: as the fact appears singular, would it not be worth while to hand over the Specimens to some good Lizardologist & Comparative Anatomist to publish an account of their internal structure.—Do what you think fit.[2]

This letter will go with a cargo of Specimens from Coquimbo. —I shall write to let you know when they are sent off.—In the Box, there are two Bags of Seeds, one ticket, Valleys of Cordilleras 5000–10000 ft high; the soil & climate exceedingly dry; soil very light & stony, extremes in temperature: the other [chiefly *added*] from the dry sandy Traversia of Mendoza 3000 ft more or

[1] See footnote to Letter 34, p. 96.

[2] Dr Sydney Smith has pointed out to me that at a meeting of the Cambridge Philosophical Society on Dec. 14, 1835, item 6 consisted of: 'communications from C. Darwin Esq., on Viviparous Lizards and on Red Snow', the Rev. Dr Clark in the Chair. The earlier geological extracts from this same letter had been read at a meeting on Nov. 16, and the decision to print the pamphlet mentioned on pp. xi–xii made at a meeting on Nov. 30. This suggests that interest had been aroused on Nov. 16, and that the last pages of the letter already partly communicated were thought worthy of notice one month later.

M. Gay's comments are given by Henslow in the original pamphlet of extracts of 1835. Although these comments do not occur in *The Voyage of the 'Beagle'*, M. Gay is mentioned in *Z*, Vol. V.

less.—If some of the bushes should grow but not be healthy, try a *slight* sprinkling of Salt & Saltpetre.—The plain is saliferous.— All the flowers in the Cordilleras appear to be Autumnal flowers. —they were all in blow & seed—many of them very pretty.—I gathered them as I rode along on the hill sides: if they will but choose to come up, I have no doubt [many *added*] would be great rarities.—In the Mendoza Bag, there are the seeds [or berrys *added*] of what appears to be a small Potatoe plant with a whitish flower. They grow many leagues from where any habitation could [have *del*] ever have existed, owing to absence of water.— Amongst the Chonos dryed plants, you will see a fine specimen of the wild Potatoe, growing under a most opposite climate & unquestionably a true wild Potatoe.—It must be a distinct species from that of the lower Cordilleras etc.—Perhaps, as with the Banana, distinct species are now not to be distinguished in their varieties, produced by cultivation.—The Beagle is not at Valparaiso. So I cannot copy out the few remarks about the Chonos Potatoe.[1]—With the Specimens, there is a bundle of old Papers & Note Books. Will you take care of them, in case I should lose my notes, these might be useful.—I do not send home any insects, because they must be troublesome to you, & now so little more of the Voyage remains unfinished I can well take charge of them.— In two or three days I set out for Coquimbo by Land, the Beagle calls for me in the middle of June: So that I have 6 weeks more to enjoy geologizing over these curious mountains of Chili.—There is at present a bloody revolution in Peru: the Commodore has gone there & in the hurry has carried our letters with him; perhaps amongst them there will be one from you.—I wish I had the old Commodore here I would shake some consideration for others into his old body.—From Coquimbo you will again hear from me.—Till then Farewell. My dear Henslow—

Yours very truly, C. Darwin

Our plans are altered. I have a ten weeks holiday & expect to

[1] The 'Chonos potato' (see Letters 46 and 49) is referred by specialists to *Solanum tuberosum* L. var. *guaytecarum* (Bitter) Hawkes, a tetraploid possibly introduced into southern Chile from Peru or Bolivia.—N. Y. S.

reach as far as Copiapo & examine all that preeminently curious country abounding with mines:—I shall not write to you, till we reach [*blank left unfilled*] excepting half a dozen lines just to inform you when my specimens leave this Port.—I am glad to say, that I believe this will be the last Cargo [with *added*] which you will be troubled.—

LETTER 39

[*To: The Rev^d. Professor Henslow Cambridge
No postmark*]

Lima July 12th. 1835

My dear Henslow

This is the last letter, which I shall ever write to you from the shores of America,—and for this reason I send it—In a few days time the Beagle will sail for the Galapagos Isds.—I look forward with joy & interest to this, both as being somewhat nearer to England, & for the sake of having a good look at an active Volcano.—Although we have seen Lava in abundance, I have never yet beheld the Crater.—I sent by H.M.S. Conway two large boxes of Specimens. The Conway sailed the latter end of June. —With them were letters for you.—Since that time I have travelled by land from Valparaiso to Copiapo & seen something more of the Cordilleras.—Some of my Geological views have been subsequently [to the last letter *added*] altered.—I believe the upper mass of strata are not so very modern as I supposed.—This last journey has explained to me much of the ancient history of the Cordilleras.—I feel sure they formerly consisted of a chain of Volcanoes from which enormous streams of Lava were poured forth at the bottom of the sea.—These alternate with sedimentary beds to a vast thickness: at a subsequent period these Volcanoes must have formed Islands, from which have been produced [strata *added*] several thousand feet [thick *added*] of coarse Conglomerate.[1]—These Islands were covered with fine trees; in the

---

[1] See *Geological Observations on South America*, London, 1846. Chap. VI: Central Chile; Structure of the Cordillera; 2nd ed. 1876. Part II.

Conglomerate I found one 15 feet in circcumference, perfectly
silicified to the very centre.—The alterations of compact crystalline rocks (I cannot doubt subaqueous Lavas) & sedimentary
beds, now upheaved, fractured & indurated, form the main range
of the Andes. The formation was produced at the time, when
Ammonites, several Terebratula, Gryphites, Oysters, Pectens,
Mytili etc etc lived.—In the central parts of Chili, the structure of
the lower beds are rendered very obscure, by the Metamorphic
action, which has rendered even the coarsest Conglomerates,
porphyritic.—The Cordilleras of the Andes so worthy of admiration from the grandeur of their dimensions, [*seem*] to rise in dignity
when it is considered that since the period of Ammonites, they
have formed a marked feature in the Geography of the Globe.—
The geology of these Mountains pleased me in one respect; when
reading Lyell, it had always struck me that if the crust of the
world goes on changing in a Circle, there ought to be somewhere
found formations which having the *age* of the great Europaean
secondary beds, should possess the *structure* of Tertiary rocks,
or those formed amidst Islands & in limited Basins. Now the
alterations of Lava & coarse sediment, which form the upper parts
of the Andes, correspond exactly to what would accumulate under
such circumstances. In consequence of this I can only very *roughly*
separate into three divisions the [varying *added*] strata (perhaps
8000 ft thick) which compose these mountains. I am afraid you
will tell me to learn my A.B.C.—to know quartz from Feldspar—
before I indulge in such speculations.—I lately got hold of report
on M. Dessalines D'Orbigny's labors in S. America: I experienced
rather a debasing degree of vexation to find he has described the
geology of the Pampas, & that I have had some hard riding for
nothing: it was however gratifying, that my conclusions are the
same, as far as I can collect, with his results.—It is also capital, that
the whole of Bolivia will be described. I hope to be able to connect
his Geology of that country, with mine of Chili.—After leaving
Copiapò, we touch at Iquique. I visited, but do not quite understand the position of the Nitrate of Soda beds.—Here in Peru,
from the state of Anarchy, I can make no expedition.—I hear

from Home, that my Brother is going to send me a box with Books & a letter from you.—It is very unfortunate that I cannot receive this before we reach Sydney, even if it ever gets safely so far.—I shall not have another opportunity for many months of again writing to you.—Will you have the charity to send me one more letter (as soon as this reaches you) directed to the C. of Good Hope. Your letters besides affording me the greatest delight always give me a fresh stimulus for exertion. Excuse this Geologico-prosy letter & Farewell till you hear from me at Sydney & see me in Autumn of 1836. Believe me, dear Henslow, Yours affectionately obliged

Charles Darwin

LETTER 40

[*To: Professor Henslow Cambridge*
From: Dr. Darwin]

28 December 1835
Shrewsbury

Dear Sir

I am much obliged for the favour of your letter, for the flattering terms in which you speak of my son and for your kind attention in sending the copies of the extracts from his letters. We are all sensible how much Charles owes to you his success and the great advantage your friendship is to him. He feels and speaks of it. I thought the voyage hazardous for his happiness but it seems to prove otherwise and it is highly gratifying to me to think he gains credit by his observation and exertion. There is a natural good humored energy in his letters just like himself.

Dear Sir very faithfully your obliged
R W Darwin

LETTER 41

[*To: The Rev.d. Profr: Henslow Cambridge*
Postmark: B Ju 22 1836]

Sydney—January—1836

My dear Henslow

This is the last opportunity of communicating with you before that joyful day when I shall reach Cambridge.—I have very little to say: But I must write if it was only to express my joy that the last year is concluded & that the present one in which the Beagle will return, is gliding onwards.—We have all been disappointed here in *not* finding even a *single* letter; we are indeed rather before our expected time, otherwise I daresay I should have seen your handwriting.—I must feed upon the future & it is beyond bounds delightful to feel the certainty that within eight months I shall be residing once again most quietly in Cambridge. Certainly I never was intended for a traveller; my thoughts are always rambling over past or future scenes; I cannot enjoy the present happiness, for anticipating the future; which is about as foolish as the dog who dropt the real bone for it's shadow.—

You see, we are now arrived at Australia: the new Continent really is a wonderful place. Ancient Rome might have boasted of such a Colony; it deserves to rank high amongst the 100 wonders of the world, as showing the Giant force of the parent country. I travelled to Bathurst, a place, 130 miles in the interior, & thus saw a little of the country.—The system of communication is carried on in an admirable style; the roads are excellent, & on the Macadam principle; to form them vast masses of rock have been cut away. The following facts, I think, very forcibly show how rapid & extraordinary is the increase of wealth.—a fraction (I believe 7/8th) of an acre [fetched by Auction *del*] of land in Sydney, fetched by Auction twelve thousand pounds; the increase of public revenue during the last year has been 68,000£.—It is well known, that there are men, who came out convicts, who now possess an yearly income of 15,000£. Is not this all wonderful? But yet I do not think this country can ever rise to be a second

North America. The sterile aspect of the land, at once proclaims
that Agriculture will never succeed.—Wool, Wool—is repeated
& must ever be the cry from one end of the country to the other.
—The scenery, from the extraordinary uniformity of its character,
is very peculiar. Every where, trees of the same class & appearance
are thinly scattered, with their upright trunks, over arid downs.
The greatest change is that in some places the fire has been more
recent & the stumps are black whilst in others, their natural color
is nearly regained.—On the whole I do not like New South
Wales: it is without doubt an admirable place to accumulate
pounds & shillings; but Heaven forfend that ever I should live,
where every other man is sure to be somewhere between a petty
rogue & bloodthirsty villain.—In a short time we sail for Hobart
town, then to K: Georges Sound, Isle of France, C. of Good Hope
etc etc England.—I last wrote to you from Lima, since which
time I have done disgracefully little in Nat: History; or rather I
should say since the Galapagos Islands, where I worked hard.—
Amongst other things, I collected every plant, which I could see
in flower, & as it was the flowering season I hope my collection
may be of some interest to you.[1]—I shall be very curious to know
whether the Flora belongs to America, or is peculiar.[2] I paid also
much attention to the Birds, which I suspect are very curious.—
The Geology to me personally was very instructive & amusing;
Craters of all sizes & forms, were studded about in every direction; some were such tiny ones, that they might be called quite

[1] In a paper by Gunnar Harling 'On some Compositae endemic to the Galapagos Islands', *Acta Horti Bergiani*, Band 20, no. 3, pp. 63-120, Uppsala, 1962,
the author considers that two species of Erigeron brought back by Darwin
should be placed in an independent new genus, Darwiniothamnus. He writes: 'It
seems very fitting to commemorate in this way Charles Darwin, who not only
brought home the type material of both species of the genus but also through his
large and excellent collections laid the foundations of our knowledge of the flora
of the Galapagos Islands.' See also Letters 44, 45, 46, 47 and 49.
    Dr Max Walters of the Cambridge Botany School called my attention to the
above paper, and also gave me every facility for examining Darwin's Galapagos
collection, still in a beautiful state of preservation due to Henslow's admirable
care.
[2] The origin and affinities of the Galapagos flora have since been discussed in
many scientific papers beginning with that of J. D. Hooker in 1847 (see footnote
on p. 129).—N. Y. S.

Specimen Craters.—There were however a few facts of interest, with respect to [streams *del*] layers of Mud or Volcanic Sandstone, which must have flowed like streams of Lava. Likewise respecting some grand fields of Trachytic Lava.—The Trachyte contained large Crystals of glassy, fractured Feldspar & the streams were naked, bare & the surface rough, as if they had flowed a week before.—I was glad to examine a kind of Lava, which I believe in recent days has not in Europe been erupted.—In our passage across the Pacifick, we only touched at Tahiti & New Zealand: at neither of these places, or at sea had I much opportunity of working.—Tahiti is a most charming spot.—Everything, which former Navigators have written is true: "A new Cytheraea has risen from the ocean". Delicious scenery, climate, manners of the people, are all in harmony. It is moreover admirable to behold what the Missionaries both here & at New Zealand have effected. —I firmly believe they are good men working for the sake of a good cause. I much suspect that those who have abused or sneered at the Missionaries, have generally been such as were not very anxious to find the Natives moral & intelligent beings.[1]—During the remainder of our voyage, we shall only visit places generally acknowledged as civilized & nearly all under the British Flag. There will be a poor field for Nat: History & without it, I have lately discovered that the pleasure of seeing new places is as nothing. I must return to my old resource & think of the future, but that I may not become more prosy I will say Farewell, till the day arrives, when I shall see my Master in Natural History & can tell him, how grateful I feel for his kindness & friendship.

Believe me Dear Henslow

Ever yours Most Faithfully Chas Darwin

[1] On the voyage between the writing of this letter in January 1836 and the arrival of H.M.S. *Beagle* at Cape Town, Darwin and FitzRoy composed a letter, signed by them both, which was published in the *South African Christian Recorder* in September 1836. It was entitled *A letter containing remarks on the Moral State of Tahiti, New Zealand*, etc., pp. 221–38.

LETTER 42

[*To: The Rev^d. Prof: Henslow* (Cambridge *del*, St. Albans *added*)
Postmark: Cambridge SE 6 1836]

St Helena. July 9th.—1836

My dear Henslow

I am going to ask you to do me a favor. I am very anxious to belong to the Geolog: Society. I do not know, but I suppose, it is necessary to be proposed some time before being balloted for, if such is the case, would you be good enough to take the proper preparatory steps. Professor Sedgwick very kindly offered to propose me, before leaving England: if he should happen to be in London, I daresay he would yet do so.—I have very little to write about. We have neither seen, done, or heard of anything particular, for a long time past: & indeed if, at present, the wonders of another planet could be displayed before us, I believe we should unanimously exclaim, what a consummate plague. No schoolboys ever sung the half sentimental & half jovial strain of "dulce domum" with more fervour, than we all feel inclined to do.—But the whole subject of dulce domum, & the delight in seeing one's friends is most dangerous; it must infallibly make one very prosy or very boisterous. Oh the degree to which I long to be once again living quietly, with not one single novel object near me.— No one can imagine it, till he has been whirled round the world, during five long years, in a ten Gun-Brig.—I am at present living in a small house (amongst the clouds) in the centre of the Isld & within stone's throw of Napoleon's tomb. It is blowing a gale of wind, with heavy rain, & wretchedly cold: if Napoleon's ghost haunts his dreary place of confinement, this would be a most excellent night for such wandering Spirits.—If the weather chooses to permit me, I hope to see a little of the Geology (so often partially described) of this Is^ds.—I suspect that differently from most Volcanic Isl^ds. its structure is rather complicated. It seems strange, that this little centre of a distinct creation should, as is asserted, bear marks of recent elevation.

The Beagle proceeds from this place to Ascencion, thence to C.

Verds (what miserable places!) to the Azores, to Plymouth & then to Home. That most glorious of all days in my life will not however arrive till the middle of October. Some time in that month, you will see me at Cambridge, when I must directly come to report myself to you, as my first Lord of the Admiralty.—At the C. of Good Hope we all on board suffered a bitter disappointment in missing nine months' letters, which are chasing us from one side of the globe to the other. I daresay amongst them was a letter from you; it is long since I have seen your hand writing, but I shall soon see you yourself, which is far better. As I am your pupil, you are bound to undertake the task of criticizing & scolding me for all the things ill done & not done at all, which I fear I shall need much; but I hope for the best, & I am sure I have a good, if not too easy, task master.—At the Cape, Capt Fitz Roy & myself enjoyed a memorable piece of good fortune in meeting Sir J. Herschel.[1]—We dined at his house & saw him a few times besides. He was exceedingly goodnatured, but his manners at first appeared to me rather awful. He is living in a very comfortable country house, surrounded by fir & oak trees, which alone, in so open a country, give a most charming air of seclusion & comfort. He appears to find time for everything; he showed us a pretty garden, full of Cape Bulbs of his own collecting; & I afterwards understood, that everything was the work of his own hands. What a very nice person Lady Herschel appears to be,—in short we were quite charmed with everything in & about the house.—There are many pleasant people at the Cape.—Mr. Maclear,[2] the astronomer, was most kind & hospitable.—I became also acquainted with Dr. A. Smith,[3] who had just returned from

[1] John Frederick William Herschel, 1792–1871, astronomer. F.R.S., 1813, Master of Mint, 1850–5. Darwin wrote of him in his *Autobiography*: 'I felt a high reverence for Sir J. Herschel. . . . He never talked much, but every word which he uttered was worth listening to. He was very shy and often had a distressed expression.'

[2] Sir Thomas Maclear, 1794–1879, Royal Astronomer at the Cape of Good Hope, 1834–70. F.R.S., 1831. The Royal Observatory was founded at the Cape in 1820.

[3] Sir Andrew Smith, 1797–1872, Director-General Army Medical Department; served at the Cape and Natal, 1821–37. Wrote on the Zoology of S. Africa. Darwin took some long geological walks with him.

his expedition beyond the Tropic of Capricorn.—He is a cap[*ital*] person & most indefatigable observer: he has brought back an immense collection, & amongst other things a new species of Rhinoceros.—If you had heard him describe his system of travelling & mode of defence, it would have recalled the days of enthusiasm, which you have told me, you felt on first reading Le Vaillant.¹—Dr. Smith shortly goes to England, he will soon return & recommence his travels & either succeed in penetrating far into the interior, or, as he says, leave his bones in Africa.—I am very stupid, & I have nothing more to say; the wind is whistling so mournfully over the bleak hills, that I shall go to bed & dream of England.—Good night, My dear Henslow
Yours most truly obliged & affectionately
Chas. Darwin.—

LETTER 43

[*To: The Revᵈ Prof: Henslow Cambridge
Postmark: Shrewsbury OC 6 1836*]

Shrewsbury Oct 6ᵗʰ.—1836
My dear Henslow
I am sure you will congratulate me on the delight of once again being home. The Beagle arrived at Falmouth on Sunday evening, & I reached Shrewsbury yesterday morning.—I am exceedingly anxious to see you, & as it will be necessary in four or five days to return to London to get my goods & chattels out of the Beagle, it appears to me my best plan to pass through Cambridge. I want your advice on many points, indeed I am in the clouds & neither know what to do, or where to go. My chief puzzle is about the geological specimens, who will have the charity to help me in describing their mineralogical nature?—Will you be kind enough to write to me one line by *return of post* saying whether you are now at Cambridge.—I am doubtful, till I hear from Capt. F. R. whether I shall not be obliged to start before the answer can arrive,

¹ François Levaillant, 1753–1824, French traveller and ornithologist. Studied in Paris, and explored S. Africa 1781–4.
I

but pray try the chance.—My dear Henslow, I do long to see you; you have been the kindest friend to me, that ever Man possessed. —I can write no more for I am giddy with joy & confusion.— Farewell for the present

Yours most truly obliged
Chas. Darwin

Thursday Morning

LETTER 44

[*To: The Revd Professor Henslow Cambridge Sunday*]

43 Great Marlborough St
30 Oct 1836

My dear Henslow
    I have delayed writing, as I daily expected the Beagle would arrive, & I should be better able to tell you how my prospects go on.—I spent yesterday on board at Greenwich, & brought back with me the Galapagos plants; they do not appear numerous, but are I hope in tolerable preservation.—Tomorrow I will procure a box & will send them to Cambridge.—I will keep this letter till I do so.—I called on your brother, but he was not at home, I left a card asking him to send anything he might happen to have, to my brothers where I am now staying.[1]—I have not made much progress with the great men; I find, as you told me, that they are all overwhelmed with their own business. Mr. Lyell has entered in the *most* goodnatured manner, & almost without being asked, into all my plans. He tells me, however, the same story, namely that I must do all myself.—Mr. Owen[2] seems anxious to dissect some of

[1] He moved into rooms of his own, 36 Great Marlborough Street, on Mar. 13, 1837.
[2] Richard Owen, 1804–92, of whom T. H. Huxley said: 'I doubt if, in the long annals of anatomy, more is to be placed to the credit of any single worker.' Born and educated at Lancaster, he soon became lecturer in anatomy in London. In 1827 he became Assistant Conservator to the Hunterian Museum under William Clift (see Letter 31, p. 83), whose daughter he married in 1835, and later sole Conservator till 1856. Hunterian Professor, 1836–56. Superintendent of Natural History Dept. of British Museum, and advocated and arranged for the separate

the animals in spirit; & besides these two I have scarcely met anyone who seems to wish to possess any of my specimens.—I must except Dr. Grant, who is willing to examine some of the corallines.—I see it is quite unreasonable to hope for a minute, that any man will undertake the examination of an whole order.— It is clear the collectors so much outnumber the real naturalists, that the latter have no time to spare.—I do not even find that the collections care for receiving the unnamed specimens.—The Zoological Museum[1] is nearly full & upward of a thousand specimens remain unmounted. I daresay the British Museum would receive them, but I cannot feel, from all I hear, any great respect even for the present state of that establishment. Your plan will be not only the best, but the only one, namely to come down to Cambridge, arrange & group together the different families & then wait till [any one *del*] people, who are already working in different branches may want specimens.—But it appears to me, to do this, it will be almost necessary to reside in London.—As far as I can yet see, my best plan will be to spend [some *del*] several months in Cambridge, & then, when by your assistance, I know on what grounds I stand, to emigrate to London, when I can complete my geology, & try *to push on the Zoology.*—I assure you I grieve to find how many things make me see the necessity of living for some time in this dirty, odious London.—[But *del*] For even in Geology, I suspect much assistance & communication will be necessary in this quarter: for instance in fossil bones of which none, excepting the fragments of Megatherium, have been looked at. And I clearly see without my presence never would be. —Fossil shells,—charts, maps, communication with Fitz Roy. Mr Lyell says also, that the power of taking any odd specimen, to

---

establishment at South Kensington. Darwin received much help from him over his specimens from the voyage; see *Ornithological Notes, Bull. B.M. (N.H.)*, Vol. 2, No. 7, pp. 223 and 244. Later Owen bitterly attacked *On the Origin of Species by means of Natural Selection* (henceforth referred to as *O*, see Abbreviations p. 24 and Bibliography p. 218) in the *Edinburgh Review*, April 1860. Darwin at first used to defend him, but later formed a low opinion of him for his ambition, envy and dishonesty. See also Letters 112 and 116 (footnote 2), pp. 203 and 209.

[1] The Museum of the Zoological Society, then at 33 Bruton Street. The collection was some years later broken up and dispersed. Footnote, *LL*, I, p. 273.

the different societies, where many Naturalists are met together is a very essential point.—However true this may be, I am very sure the assistance I shall get in Cambridge will be infinitely more, than I ever should receive in London.—Prof. Sedgwick very kindly hunted out my quarters, & I breakfasted with him.—I am sorry to find he will leave Cambridge so soon.—From the delay in the Beagle's arrival, I do not know whether I shall be able to come down before the end of the month, for I have yet to visit Shrewsbury.—If you have opportunities, talk a little with him on those points you said his advice would be most valuable; namely the form of publication. I think from what I hear, that a volume, would be less troublesome & pleasanter, than detached papers.— Also about fossil shells. Is Sowerby a good man? I understand his assistance can be purchased.—Mr. Clift says he will ask Prof. Buckland to look at the bones; I should think he would rather like it, as Mr. Clift says some belong to forms [which *added*] he [himself *added*] does not at all know.—I am anxious to know, whether Prof. Sedgwick recommends any particular nomenclature for the rocks.—I have often thought of your really most kind offer of talking with Mrs. Henslow about my taking up my quarters with you. Few things could give me more happiness, & at the same time do me more real good. But I fear I should be much in the way, & I have been thinking of another plan which would be better for the work; that is to take lodgings, with two sitting rooms & a bedroom, (which I daresay could be procured), in one of which my servant could work & it would at the same time serve for a warehouse for the skins etc etc etc.—Perhaps my servant might live in the house.—In college I should only have one room, which although a large one, would be inconvenient; and as it may turn out more advisable not to remain a whole year, it is a great expence to buy furniture, crockery etc etc etc for any shorter period. If I subsequently live in London, I shall follow my brothers [plan *added*] take the whole of an unfurnished house, excepting the shop or office, then furnish two rooms, & keep the others for lumber.—Such a house can be got for less than 100£ per annum. I believe Mr. Ash [clearly *added*] understood it was

quite a chance, whether I intended coming to reside the whole
year. If you should happen to meet him (but otherwise not) just
mention that I shall probably not reside for such a time, & he will
then understand, that I should not trouble him about rooms.—

I find this letter, which is a most unmerciful long one all about
myself, extending over so much paper, that I will send it with the
plants, & write another just to forewarn you of the Box. Perhaps
also I shall be able by that time to [send *del*] announce the heavy
cases with geolog. & other specimens. Would it not be the best
plan, *if it can be so managed*, to leave the heavy geolog: boxes at
the warehouse, so that when [I come down & *added*] the room is
ready, to take them direct there? I have forgotten to mention one
bad bit of news, namely that Cuming[1] was at the Galapagos.—
Did he collect plants. I doubt it, because the [far *added*] greater
part of the plants only live near the summit of the mountains, some
miles from the coast? I shall grieve if you lose your tiny botanical
feast,—I only wish I had known the Botanists cared so much for
specimens & the Zoologists so little; the proportional number of
specimens in the two branches should have [worn *del*] had a very
different appearance. I am out of patience with the Zoologists,
not because they are overworked, but for their mean quarrelsome
spirit. I went the other evening to the Zoological Soc. where the
speakers were snarling at each other, in a manner anything but
like [that of *added*] gentlemen. Thank Heaven, as long as I
remain in Cambridge there will not be any danger of falling into
any such contemptible quarrels, whilst in London I do not see
how it is to be avoided. Of the Naturalists; F. Hope[2] is out of

---

[1] Hugh Cuming, 1791–1865, naturalist; sail-maker in Valparaiso, 1819.
Collected shells in the Pacific, off the coast of Chili, Philippine Islands, etc.
Returned to England in 1839. Darwin made good use of Cuming's facts on the
island distribution of shells when writing up his material.

Cuming collected a few plants in 1829 on the Galapagos Islands. They are
embodied, with Darwin's, in J. D. Hooker's 'Enumeration of the Plants of the
Galapagos Archipelago' in *Trans. Linn. Soc.*, Vol. XX, 1847, pp. 163–233.—
N. Y. S.

[2] F. W. Hope, 1797–1862, entomologist and collector, founded a zoological
professorship at Oxford; left his collections to the University. President of the
Entomological Society 1835 and 1846.

London, Westwood[1] I have not seen; so about my insects I know nothing.—I have seen Mr. Yarrel[2] twice, but he is so evidently so oppressed with business, that it is too selfish to plague him with my concerns. He has asked me to dine with the Linnaean on Tuesday; & on Wednesday I dine with Geolog: so that I shall see all the great men.—Mr. Bell[3] I hear is so much occupied that there is no chance of his wishing for specimens of reptiles.—I have forgotten to mention Mr. Lonsdale,[4] who gave me a most cordial reception, & with whom I had much most interesting conversation.—If I was not much more inclined for geology, than the other branches of Natural History, I am sure Mr. Lyell's & Londsdale [s] kindness ought to fix me.—You cannot conceive anything more thoroughly goodnatured, than the heart & soul manner, in which he put himself in my place & thought what would be best to do.—At first he was all for London versus Cambridge, but at last I made him confess that for some time at least the latter would be for me much the best. There is not another soul, whom I could ask, excepting yourself, to wade through & criticize [those *del*] some of those papers which I have left with you.—Mr. Lyell owned that second to London, there was no place in England, so good for a naturalist as Cambridge. Upon my word I am ashamed of writing so many foolish details; no young lady ever described her first ball with more particularity. —With respect to the mathematical instruments, I told the Captain I was sure you would allow him to leave the boxes for a week or two longer till he was established & knew where to have them directed to.

[1] J. O. Westwood, 1805–93, first Hope Professor of Zoology, Oxford, 1861–1891; entomological and palaeological works.

[2] See footnote 1 to Letter 10, p. 40.

[3] Thomas Bell, 1792–1880, dental surgeon: F.R.S., 1828; lecturer on comparative anatomy; Professor of Zoology, King's College, London, 1836; F.R.C.S., 1844. Became Secretary of the Royal Society, and President of the Linnean Society. Published *A History of British Reptiles*, 1839, and other zoological works. Thomas Bell did ultimately take over the volume on *Reptiles*, published in 1843 as Vol. V of *Z*, edited and superintended by Charles Darwin. See following letters.

[4] William Lonsdale, 1794–1871; Curator and Librarian of the Geological Society, 1829–42.

Monday evening— I have determined to send the plants by wagon with the bird skins for reason which you will know by the letter which announces the boxes.

Yours ever most sincerely
Chas Darwin

Again I have been compelled to change my plans.—I send the plants per coach, & this letter with them.—I will also write one line by the post in case of any accident. On Thursday the four boxes will arrive at Cambridge by Marsh's Wagon.—

LETTER 45

[*To: The Rev^d. Prof Henslow Cambridge*
Postmark: EX 2 No 2 1836]

43 Great Marlborough St.
Tuesday Evening [*2 Novr. 1836*]

My dear Henslow

You will have probably received, before this letter reaches you, the box with the Galapagos plants, which also contains a longer letter. The box starts tomorrow morning by the Fly Coach.— Four boxes were also sent by [the *del*] Marsh's Wagon today— they will reach Cambridge on Thursday morning.—The two very heavy & largest ones contain geological specimens; if it could be so arranged would it not be better to leave them in the warehouse, in such case pray see that they are so placed as not to be moved, & that they are housed dry.—The smallest box contains spirit cases; the square one bird skins & insects. These perhaps had better be carried away into safety.—I have just returned from dining at the Linnaean club & attending [pap *del*] a meeting to hear a couple of intensely stupid papers.—I became acquainted with Mr. Bell, who, to my surprise, expressed a good deal of interest about my crustaceae & reptiles & seems willing to work at them.—I also heard, that Mr. Broderip would be glad to look over the S. American shells.—So that things flourish well with me.—You have made me known amongst the botanists; but

I felt very foolish, when Mr. Don[1] remarked on the beautiful appearance of some plant with an astoundingly long name, & asked me about its habitation. Some-one else seemed quite surprised that I knew nothing about a carex from I do not know where. I was at last forced to plead most intire innocence,—that I knew no more about the plants which I had collected, than the Man in the Moon.—Pray write me a line to say how the Cambridge world is going on; & whether my boxes arrive safely.— Tell me whether you are disappointed with the Galapagos plants. I have some fears.—Pray remember me most kindly to Mrs Henslow.—I long to be again in Cambridge.—Believe me

Yours ever most truly obliged
Chas Darwin

LETTER 46

[*To: The Rev*^d *Professor Henslow Cambridge*
Postmark: MR 28 1837]

36 Great Marlborough St.
March 28th. 1837

My dear Henslow

I have been very idle in not writing to you sooner, but I have been waiting to see if anything particular should occur to write about. But such has not been the case.—I am living very quietly in nice comfortable lodgings, and though I sadly miss a good walk in the country I am pretty well resigned to my fate. Till within the few last days I have been to as many dinner parties, as at your riotous place of Cambridge, but now I am in the way of being left alone. I do not think when I last saw you, that our plans about publication were settled. Now the scheme [*is*] that the Captain makes a plumpudding out of his own journal and that of Capt. King's kept during the last voyage, which together will make two volumes and the third I am to have to myself. I intend making it in a journal form, but following the order of places

1 David Don, 1800–41. Professor of Botany, King's College, London, 1836–41. Librarian to the Linnean Society.

rather than that of time, giving results of my geology and habits
of animals where interesting.—I have been going steadily and
have already made a hole in the work, which I fear is more than
the Captain can say. We intend to publish on the first of November, but I doubt it will not be ready. As soon as I have gone
straight through the journal, I shall [begin and *del*] continue adding what I can by studying the geographical range and other such
subjects of the different branches. I daresay by the middle of the
summer, you will [have time to *added*] give me some general remarks, which will much add to the value of the whole.—I met
Mr. Brown[1] a few days after you had called on him, he asked me
in rather an ominous manner what I meant to do with my plants.
—In the course of conversation Mr. Broderip who was present
remarked to him "you forget how long it is since Capt. King's
expedition." He answered, "Indeed I have something, in the
shape of Capt. King's undescribed plants to make me recollect
it." Could a better reason be given [if I had been asked *added*] by
me for not giving the plants to the Brit. Museum.—Mr. Brown
also said [that *added*] *you* must recollect that there are plants
from the Galapagos Isds. at the Brit. Museum. It would be well
to find out what they are.—How goes on the new University?[2]
I hear the examiners are to be paid, I trust you will be one, &
will thus pay the great city more frequent visits.—Pray remember me most kindly to Leonard J,[3] tell him he will be glad for
my sake to hear that Mr. Bell is willing to undertake my reptiles

[1] Robert Brown, 1773–1858, educated Aberdeen and Edinburgh. Naturalist to
Flinders' Australasian expedition, 1801–5. Librarian to Linnean Society. First
Keeper of Botany in the British Museum. Published botanical works. A man
jealous of his own discoveries, whom Darwin saw much of in these years. See
Autobiography, p. 103. Humboldt referred to him as 'Botanicorum facile princeps'.
[2] This must refer to the University of London. The early history of University
College, London, began in 1825, when Thomas Campbell, the poet, and others,
initiated the plan so as to include dissenters who were practically excluded from
the older universities; the seven acres now constituting the site of University
College were bought, and the first stone laid in 1827. By 1831 King's College
was incorporated, to include in their teaching 'the doctrines and teachings of
Christianity'. In 1836 there were further adjustments, and both University College
and King's College were incorporated in the University. The charters were
signed on November 28, 1836—four months before the writing of this letter.
[3] Leonard Jenyns, Henslow's brother-in-law.

and the higher order of the Crustacea. Will you ask Leonard if he will look at the few Galapagos fish first, that is if it does not quite break through the order in which the whole will be examined. The dried fish, I believe, nearly all come from those islands. Will you keep a [page in a *added*] memorandum book for queries from me? I will begin with two or three.—Name of plant (   )¹ from Fernando Noronha. The name of the Cardoon?—I found it out in Isabelle's voyages, but have forgotten it. He calls it also the Cardoon of Spain.—Do you know what is the giant thistle of the Pampas?²—At some future time I shall want to know number [*of*] species of plants at Galapagos and Keeling, and at the latter whether seeds sent probably endure floating on salt water. I suppose after a little more examination you would be able to say what was the general character of the vegetation of the Galapagos? Pray take in hand as soon as your lectures are over, the potato from the Chonos Islds.—When you next meet Prof. Miller,³ pray [tel *del*] remember me to him and tell him I shall not look at any more geological specimens for a few months, so that there is not the slightest hurry about the specimens which he has of mine.—Will you give my direction, in case he ever should have a spare half hour, when in town.—Have you ever had an opportunity of sounding any of the great Cambridge Dons about the publication of my geology. I hope they will prove gracious for it would be a great bore to be half killed with seasickness, and then in reward half starved with poverty. The postman's bell is ringing so I must close this letter; with my best thanks for all your kindness Dear Henslow

Yours ever most truly
Chas Darwin

Pray remember me most kindly to Mrs. Henslow

¹ Unfilled bracket left by Charles Darwin.

² The 'giant thistle of the Pampas', or 'Cardoon', is *Cynara cardunculus* L., which is very frequent there, and known as 'cardo de Castilla' or 'cardón'. See p. 133, Letter 50.—N. Y. S.

³ William Hallowes Miller, 1801–80, Professor of Mineralogy at Cambridge, 1832–70.

LETTER 47

36 Grt Marlborough Street 18th—
[*May 1837*]

My dear Henslow

I was very glad to receive your letter. I wanted much to hear how you were getting on with your manifold labours.—Indeed I do not wonder your head began to ache; it is almost a wonder you have any head left.—Your account of the Gamblingay expedition was cruelly tempting, but I cannot anyhow leave London.—I wanted to pay my good dear people at Shrewsbury a visit of a few days, but I found I could not manage it.—At present I am waiting for the signatures of the Duke of Somerset as President of the Linnaean; [of *added*] Ld. Derby & Whewell,[1] to a statement of the value of my collection; the instant I get this I shall apply to government, for assistance in engraving & to publish the Zoology on some uniform plan.—It is quite ridiculous the time any operation requires, which depends on many people.—Mr. Brown has been taking a good deal of interest in my affairs & in a most kind manner. I want therefore to oblige him any way I can.—He was much pleased with the fossil woods & has gone to the expence of having several of them cut & ground.—The clump of trees which were growing vertically [were fine *del*, are *added*] allied to Araucaria, but in some respects resembling yews.—Some of the good wise people, till seeing the wood, thought I [was *del*] had mistaken *calcareous concretions* for [silicified *added*] trees!— Mr. Brown is very curious about the fungi from the beech trees in T. del Fuego.—He has some specimens, but is very curious to see mine, but I do not know whether he wants to describe them: as your hands are so full, would you object to send them to me, & allow Mr. Brown to do what he likes with them.—If you particularly care about them, of course do not send them, but otherwise I should be glad to oblige Mr. Brown.—I have introduced

[1] See footnote to Letter 31, p. 87.

my imperfect account of them in my journal,—so that I should
for my own sake be glad of Mr. Brown's inspection *soon*.—[1]

I have been working very steadily, but have only got two
thirds through the journal part alone.—I find, though I remain
daily many hours at work, the progress is very slow:—it is an
awful thing to say to oneself, every fool and every clever man in
England, if he chooses, may make as many illnatured remarks as
he [can *del*] likes on this unfortunate sentence.

There is a very *remote* possibility of my publishing my part before
the Captains, in which case it would be out this summer.[2] There
are [one *del*] about half a dozen plants of which if I do not know
the names of genus or something about them, I must strike out
long passages in my journal.—Will you have the kindness to tell
me, a week or ten days before you leave Cambridge; so that those
questions which are most indispensible to me, perhaps you would
not grudge one day in answering.—This is in case I publish before autumn, otherwise when you return will be soon enough for
me.—I have not begun my geology *yet*!! though indeed I have
been far from idle.—I give abstracts in my journal [which *added*]
cost much time.—I am greatly obliged to you, for talking to the
Dons about the publication of my geology; the more I see of
things the greater difficulty I anticipate on any other method.—
Having seen a very great deal of Lyell, who is a most kind friend,
I entertain great hopes that my geology will be of service.—I
grieve to hear that the London University scheme will not bring
you often to London.—But I will pay Cambridge a visit before

[1] See also Letters 48 and 49. The fungus was not described by Robert Brown,
but by the Rev. M. J. Berkeley, *Linn. Trans.*, Vol. XIX, p. 37, and named
Cyttaria darwinii. Beautifully preserved specimens still exist in the Botany School,
Cambridge (1963). With regard to the silicified wood, Darwin wrote to L.
Jenyns on April 10, 1837: 'Tell Henslow, I think my silicified wood has unflinted
Mr. Brown's Heart, for he was very gracious to me, and talked about the Gala-
pagos plants; but before he never would say a word.' See *LL*, I, p. 282.

[2] This possibility was not realised. Darwin's *Journal of Researches* was first
published as Vol. III of *Narrative of the Surveying Voyages of His Majesty's Ships
Adventure and Beagle* in 1839, the delay caused by FitzRoy's procrastination. This
volume had a separate reprinting under the title *Journal of Researches in Geology
and Natural History*. John Murray's subsequent editions of 1845 and 1860 contained considerable and final alterations. See Bibliography, p. 218.

very long & we will have one more of those good walks, that I used often to think of at the antipodes, as indeed I now do.— Eyton is up here and working famously.—He tells me to say that he has bought Freycinet's *Voyage of l'Uranie* and that he has 120 folio [uncoloured *added*] plates and a quarto of letter press with a few pages imperfect at beginning; & he says anyone may have them for three pounds.—I forgot to ask you: if I succeed with government & if afterwards it appears advisable, should you object to publish the botany of the Galapagos in it, as part of the fauna?—I certainly should like, if possible, some part of the botany kept together when there are materials for any general result[*s*].[1]—Dont trouble yourself to answer this letter, for every five minutes must be precious to you.—Pray remember me most kindly to Mrs. Henslow.

Ever yours most truly
C. Darwin

[*added at beginning of letter*] Remember me to L. Jenyns.—I daresay he is with you this very day at Gamblingay.—I wish I was: how pleasant a good ramble would be in those nice woods. If you decide to send the fungi will you send them soon by coach.—

---

[1] The botanical collections from the voyage were finally handed over to Henslow's son-in-law, Joseph Hooker. Hooker's published records are as follows: 'Enumeration of the Plants of the Galapagos Islands with descriptions of the new species', *Proc. Linn. Soc.*, Vol. I, 1846, pp. 276–9; *Trans. Linn. Soc.* Vol. XX, 1847, pp. 163–234. Also: 'Vegetation of Galapagos Archipelago as compared with that of some other tropical islands, and of the continent of America', *Proc. Linn. Soc.*, Vol. I, 1847, pp. 313–14; *Trans. Linn. Soc.*, Vol. XX, 1847, pp. 235–62. The main part of the dried specimens are still kept in the Botany School, Cambridge. Duplicates of Darwin's specimens are at Kew, and some also at Manchester, Missouri and Paris.

LETTER 48

[*To: The Revd Prof Henslow Cambridge*
No postmark]

28. May 1837

My dear Henslow

I am very much obliged to you for thinking of sending me up the chart and account of Diego Garcia.[1]—It is a beautiful instance of a Lagoon Island—but I was previously aware of its existence. —On Wednesday I am going to read a short account of my views of the whole affair; and Lyell I believe intends giving up the crater doctrine,—so that I am just at present full of interest on the subject.—I fear by your letter you cared more about the edible Fungi than I thought.—I took them to Mr. Brown, who said he had never seen anything of the sort before, & appeared interested on the subject, but whether he means to describe [to *del*] them, & for what he wants them,—I have not a guess,—at some future time, if I can summon courage, I will ask him, but I stand in great awe of Robertus Brown.—I forgot to say I hope you will express my thanks to Mr. Parker, for his kindness in so readily forwarding the chart;—I know of no particular questions to ask; as the only one [of which I am very anxious *added*] that of subsidence, would require a very guarded examination on the spot, with such ideas in view.—I have told Eyton you would take [Eyton who *del*] Freycinet, & he now tells me he has the whole of the letter press; which I send together with this letter. Since writing last, our plans about publishing are become definite with respect to time.— I shall begin to print in the beginning of August: [and *del*] but the whole will not be published till November 1st.—The questions about plants are very few in number which I want answered and

---

[1] See Darwin's *Coral Reefs*, third edition, 1889, pp. 90–5. Darwin discusses the submergence of these islands of the Indian Ocean, and on the evidence then available suggests: 'We must look to some other cause than the rate of growth; and I suspect it will be found in the reefs being formed of different species of corals, adapted to live at different depths', p. 94. See also Appendix IV, p. 234, by D. R. Stoddart.

I will copy them out on the other side.—A man ought to go round the world two or three times to learn experience. I suspect I have begun at the wrong end, I ought to have published detailed Geology & Zoology first, & then all general views might have come out in as perfect a form as the subject permitted.— Now the first book will consist of mere series of imperfect sketches.—But it cannot be helped, & I am determined not to plague myself about it. Things shall take their course, and I will do as well as I can.—I will copy out the list of Botanical questions on a separate piece of paper.—I have been paying the Beagle a visit today. She sails in a week for Australia. It appeared marvellously odd to see the little vessel—and to think that I should not be one of the party.—If it was not for the sea sickness, I should have no objection to start again.—I envy you people in the country; even the smoky gardens near Greenwich looked quite beautiful, so fresh & green.—

Yours ever most truly
Chas. Darwin—

N.B. If you should ever have an opportunity, will you send one of those junctions of the Parasitical bush[1] & Beech, which I brought home for Mr. Brown.—I have always forgotten it.—

LETTER 49

[To: The Revd Prof Henslow Cambridge
Postmark: B Jy 13 1837]

36 Grt. Marlbro' St.
Thursday 14 July 1837

My dear Henslow

I returned a few days since from my Shrewsbury visit, which I enjoyed most thoroughly, I am now hard at work, cramming up

---

[1] The 'parasitical bush' was a species of *Myzodendron*, a remarkable genus, sole representative of the family *Myzodendraceae*. The species are parasitic on species of *Nothofagus* (Southern Beech). Darwin's specimen of *M. brachystachyum* DC., collected on Tierra del Fuego, is in the Kew Herbarium.—N. Y. S.

learning to ornament my journal with; you may guess the object of this letter is to beg a few hard names, respecting my plants.—I believe I shall really begin printing in beginning of August, so that there is no time to lose.—Will you look over the list of questions, & [an *del*] try to answer me some of them.—For instance it will not take you long just to count the number of species in my collection from the Keeling Isds:—You can tell me something about the Galapagos plants, without any further examination:—You can tell me what genus of fungi the edible one from T. del Fuego comes nearest to; Mr. Brown of course has not only never looked at it a second time, but cannot even lay his hand on the specimens.—I fear I must trouble you to send me one more *good* dried specimen, for I am thinking of having a wood cut.— [To examine *added*] The potatoe from Chonos would not take you long; & it is probable you already know the name of some insignificant little plants, ([which *del*] the numbers of which are in the list of questions) which go to form the peat of that country.— Pray remember today is the 12th.—I know if possible you will answer the questions.—Will you ask Leonard Jenyns whether he can tell me the genus of little fish, which I believe is a Diodon (132). It [was *del*] is the only fish I care about the name; but I am far from certain it is one of those preserved, or whether it was thrown away. I suppose all your business about the living is settled, & that you will not have occasion to come up to London again.—I am getting heartily sick of my journal & wish it was finished that I might set to work at the geology.—You do not know what a comfort it is to me to know that the proof sheets will pass under your eye, before they are published.

Ever yours most truly
Chas. Darwin

'Fuegians going to trade their children as slaves with the Patagonians'
Voyages of the Beagle, vol. II, p. 171

'Breast ploughing at Chiloe'
Voyages of the Beagle, vol. I, p. 287

LETTER 50

[*To: The Rev^d. Prof: Henslow, Hitcham, Bildeston, Suffolk.*]

[*Crossed out and redirected to Cambridge, with 'Left Hitcham' written above. Date on postmark illegible*]

36 Grt Marlborough St.^t—
Tuesday Aug: 1837

My dear Henslow

I am going to plague you about the thistles; I verily believe no rider on the Pampas was ever more tormented by the living plants, than [I *del*] you have been by the dried ones.—I send my MSS to the press the day after tomorrow, but not the part with the thistles, which will [come next *del*] go a few days afterward— My question is this—as D'Orbigny says that both the Cynara cardunculus and artichoke are wild, I had better, I should think, merely speak of the genus Cynara.—D'Orbigny says the third kind of thistle is [allied *added*] Eryngium bromelifolium: now can you tell me, would this plant resemble an overgrown sowthistle, —prickly [green *added*] leaves, veined with white.[1]—I am very glad the election went off well. I am afraid amidst all the turmoil you would have hardly been able to have looked at my plants.— Pray write *soon* & tell me whether you can answer me any of the questions; so that I may know.—I should count first, the two or three about *America*. I do not think I added to the list, whether it was from Port Desire that the radishes, turnips & carrots came.— You will see that I have been impe[r]tinent enough to pay the postage.—But otherwise I could not with a good conscience have made any man [tell *del*] pay eight pence for telling me whether an Eryngium would by common mortals be called a giant sow thistle—

In less than a fortnight I hope to send you my first proof sheet,

---

[1] A number of tall species of *Eryngium*, known as 'carda' or 'cardón', occur on the Pampas but Darwin may be referring to the Milk Thistle, *Silybum marianum* (L.) Gaertn., which is also very frequent there and known as 'cardo asnal'.— N. Y. S.

K

for you to skim your eye over.—Mr. Colburn[1] to save expence, has got one of his *hacks* to read over my MSS, [who *del*, & *added*] he has pointed out some trifling inaccuracies, so I hope it wont [be *added*] much more trouble to you than reading [it *added*] which as you *sent* me out you know you are bound to do.—Pray tell me whether you expect to be living tranquilly at Hitcham during the next month,—

My dear Henslow
Ever yours
C. Darwin

LETTER 51

*[To: The Rev*ᵈ*. Professor Henslow, Hitcham, Bildeston, Suffolk Postmark: V AU 17 1837]*

August 16th 1837

My dear Henslow

I have delayed writing to you, to thank you most sincerely, for having so effectually managed my affair. I waited till I had had an interview, with the Chancellor of the Exchequer.[2]—He appointed to see me this morning, & I had a long conversation with him, Mr. Peacocke being present. Nothing could be more thoroughly obliging & kind than his whole manners.—He made no sort of restriction, but only told me to make the most of [*the*] money, which of course I am right willing to do. I expected rather an awful interview, but I never found anything less so in my life. It will be my fault if I do not make a good work; but I sometimes

[1] Henry Colburn, Great Marlborough St., who in 1839 published *The Narrative of the Surveying Voyages of His Majesty's Ships Adventure and Beagle between the years 1826 and 1836 etc.* Vol. III contains Darwin's account of the second voyage.

[2] Thomas Spring Rice, 1790–1866, first Baron Monteagle of Brandon in Kerry, 1839. Secretary to Treasury in Grey's administration, 1830–4; Chancellor of the Exchequer, 1835–9. in Melbourne's second administration. Darwin's interview was about obtaining a Treasury grant of £1,000 for the publication of Z in five volumes, edited by Darwin. His collaborators were: Part I, *Fossil Mammalia*, Richard Owen; Part II, *Mammalia*, George R. Waterhouse; Part III, *Birds*, John Gould and G. R. Gray; Part IV, *Fish*, L. Jenyns; Part V, *Reptiles*, Thomas Bell.

take awful fright I have not materials enough.—It will be excessively satisfactory at the end of some two years to find all materials made the most they were capable of.—

I received the box with the fungus & peat plant.—I could find out nothing about the latter at the Linnaean Society but Mr. Bennet at the British Museum, soon made it out. It is *Astelia* (?) *pumila* of Brown.[1]—*Anthericum trifarium* of Solander.—I really hope in the course of a week to have some proof sheets, but there has been an unavoidable delay on the part of the printers. I saw Leonard Jenyns on Monday, and had a walk about the streets with him, & had a great deal of talk about all sorts of things. I wish I may be able to go to Liverpool;[2] there will be so many there whom I should like to meet. But if it delays my book a week, nothing shall induce me to go; for I do long to see it printed & done for.—

The next time you hear from me probably it will be with a proof sheet.—I must once again thank you my dear Henslow, you have been [the *added*] making of me, from the first. I never should [*have*] cared much for Natural History if it had not been for your friendship, when I was at Cambridge. You helped to keep me up to the mark all the voyage, & now you have completed the whole, by helping me to make the most of the results.—If it had not been for you *alone* I should never have got the 1000£. My dear Henslow, I am most truly obliged.

Chas. Darwin

[1] The correct citation of this species is *Astelia pumila* (Forster) Gaudichaud.— N. Y. S.

[2] The British Association met at Liverpool in 1837, under the presidency of the Earl of Burlington, F.R.S., later Duke of Devonshire.

LETTER 52

[*To: The Rev^d. Prof. Henslow, Hitcham, Bildeston, Suffolk*
Postmark: Paid 20 Sept 20 1837 Post Paid]

36 Great Marlborough St.
Wednesday 20 Sept 1837

My dear Henslow

I have not been very well of late with an uncomfortable palpitation of the heart, and my doctors urge me *strongly* to knock off all work & go and live in the country for a few weeks.—I believe I must do this: but I am in a puzzle how to go on correcting the press.—If the proof is first sent to me, & then to you, & then to me again at Shrewsbury, very much time will be lost; and, even as is it [*it is*] the Printers are always plaguing me, saying they are unable to print the work quickly (which I urgently desire) if I keep so many sheets in type. I cannot tell whether it will be best for the proof to go first to you & thence to me or vice versâ.—In the latter case I lose the advantage of any sweeping criticisms, such as altering the tone of any whole page.—Whilst, on the other hand, if it goes to you first, I fear it must give you more trouble. Could you look over the proof [& *added*] without troubling yourself with minutiae, & correcting such as you now do, leave me to finish the job.—When you offered to look over my proof sheets, I had not then experience, & did not know what a troublesome but goodnatured office you undertook.—I find it most disagreeable work: if I attend to sense, I forget the spelling, & vice versâ.—Will you have the goodness to write to me by return of post & tell me what appears best to you.—For I feel I must have a little rest, else I shall break down.—I want also to hear whether you had time to speak to Mr. Sp. Rice.[1] The slips from Liverpool, arrived by the *twopenny* post last night, but my printers bullied me so, that I was obliged to send [the *del*] a duplicate proof, before I received. Some of your corrections I have been able to put in [in *del*] the revise. With respect to quantity of vegetation on plains & forests, I never saw a primeval forest, that

[1] See Letter 51.

was not an impenetrable jungle, whereas the plains of S. Africa are open, although no doubt, as you suggest, a plain *thickly* covered with [*growth*] 8 or 11 ft. high would supply in [*new*] accessible quantity as much as (or more than) the thickest jungle.— But I suppose you agree in the general fact, that geologists have been hasty in their conclusions. I have corrected three or four slips & sent them direct to the bothering printers. I trust in Providence, there were not many errors. I must take my chance for two or three more, for I hope to leave London (if I can manage it) on Monday, so that there will not be time to send them to you & receive them back. You will find a jump in the next you look over. —Will you tell me about your post; when shall you receive this (sent on Wednesday) & how soon would you be able to forward [it *del*] anything to Shrewsbury? I would not be giving trouble by changing my plans, if I did not feel it was necessary. My dear Henslow Ever your's C.D. I have just received a proof which I send in hope it will be back by Saturday, I have kept a duplicate.

LETTER 53

[*To: The Rev^d. Prof. Henslow, Hitcham, Bildestone, Suffolk*
Post Paid.
Postmark: PAID, 23SE23 1837]

Saturday 23 Sept 1837

My dear Henslow

I am greatly obliged to you for allowing me to send the slips to you first; for now all will go on capitally.—I shall leave London on Monday & shall tell the printers henceforward to send the slip to you.—I will keep an account of how many you receive. In case you should be busy or unwell [etc *added*] & have not time to look over the slip any day, I think it will be best to forward it [blank *del*] uncorrected & not keep it, for the printers are so savage. I only pray that all readers are not so sharp-sighted as you, otherwise they will I fear find a good many errors in the slips which I sent whilst you were at Liverpool.—What a very difficult thing it is to write correctly, I am only just beginning to feel my own inaccuracies. The slip I send by this post, is [not *del*] corrected all but a column and a half. Will you forward it to Shrewsbury.—

I am sorry you should have had the trouble of writing to Mr. Rice. My father wants to see me, else I know nothing I should have enjoyed more than paying you a visit & to "see how comfortable you are".—I have been working all day till I am quite tired.

Yours most truly   Chas. Darwin

Remember me most kindly to Mrs Henslow, & give my best love to my dear little grave Miss Anny.—

LETTER 54

[*To: The Rev^d. Professor Henslow, Hitcham, Bildeston, Suffolk. Single Post Paid*
Postmark: C PAID 16 OC 16 1837]

October 14th 1837

My dear Henslow

Pray do not take fright at the size of this letter: but first for business.—I have written to the printer to tell him not to send the slips after the post of the 18th, to Hitcham. I leave Shrewsbury for Staffordshire on Thursday evening. Therefore will you send the slips *after* your post on Tuesday to 36 Grt. Marlborough St: where I shall arrive at the end of the week.—

I am much obliged to you for your message about the Secretaryship: I am exceedingly anxious for you to hear my side of the question; & will [you *added*] be so kind as afterwards to give me your fair judgment.—The subject has [fairly *del*] haunted me all summer. I am [loth *del*] unwilling to undertake the office for the following reasons.—1st. My entire ignorance of English Geology, [a knowledge of *added*] which would be almost necessary in order to shorten many of the papers before reading them, [before the Society *added*], or rather to know which parts to skip.—Again my ignorance of all languages; & not knowing how to pronounce even a *single* word of French,—a language so perpetually quoted. It would be disgraceful to the Society to have a Secretary who

could not read French. 2nd. The loss of time. Pray consider, that
I shall have [to *added*] look after the artists, superintend & furnish
materials for the government work, which will come out in parts,
& which must appear regularly. All my geological notes are in a
very rough state, none of my fossil shells worked up, & I have
much to read. I have had hopes by giving up society & not wast-
ing an hour, that I should be able to finish my geology in a year &
a half, by which time the descriptions of the higher animals by
others would be completed & my whole time would then necessarily be required to complete myself the description of the invertebrate ones. If this plan fails, as the government work must
go on, the geology would necessarily be deferred till probably at
least three years from this time.

   In the present state of the science, a great part of the utility of
the little I have done, would be lost, & all freshness & pleasure
quite taken from me. I know from experience the time required to
make abstracts, [even *added*] of my own papers, for the Proceedings. If I was secretary & had to make double abstracts of each
paper, studying them before reading; and attendance, would *at*
least cost me three days [(& often more) *added*] in the fortnight.
There are likewise other accidental & contingent losses of time.—
I know Dr. Royle found the office consumed much of his time.
—If by merely giving up any amusement, or by working harder
than I have done, I could save time, I would undertake the
secretaryship, but I appeal to you, whether, with my slow manner
of writing,—with two works in hand,—& with the certainty if I
cannot complete the geological part within a fixed period, that
its publication must be retarded for a very long time, whether any
Society whatever has any claim on me for three days' disagreeable
work every fortnight. I cannot agree that it is a *duty* on my part,
as a follower of science, as long as I devote myself to the completion of the work I have in hand, to delay that by undertaking
what may be done by any person who happens to have more
spare time than I have [at present *added*]. Moreover so EARLY in
my scientific life, with so very much as I have to learn, the office,
though no doubt a great honour etc for me, would be the more

burdensome. Mr. Whewell,[1] I know very well, judging from himself, will think I exaggerate the time the secretaryship would require, but I absolutely know the time, which with me the simplest writing consumes. I do not at all like appearing so selfish as to refuse Mr. Whewell, more especially as he has always shewn, in the kindest manner, an interest in my affairs.—But I cannot look forward with even tolerable comfort to undertaking an office without entering in it heart & soul, & that would be impossible with the Government work & the geology in hand. My last objection is that I doubt how far my health will stand the confinement of what I have to do without any additional work. I merely repeat, that you may know I am not speaking idly, that when I consulted Dr. Clark in town, he at first urged me to give up entirely all writing, and even correcting press for some weeks. Of late, anything which flurries me completely knocks me up afterwards and brings on a violent palpitation of the heart. Now the Secretaryship would be a periodical source of more annoying trouble to me, than all the rest of the fortnight put together. In fact till I return to town and see how I get on, if I wished the office ever so much, I *could* not say I would positively undertake it. I beg of you to excuse this very long prose all about myself; but the point is one of great interest,—I can neither bear to think myself very selfish and sulky, nor can I see the possibility of my taking the secretaryship with making a sacrifice of all my plans, and a good deal of comfort.—If you see Whewell, would you tell him the substance of this letter; or if he will take the trouble, he may read it.—

My dear Henslow, I appeal to you in loco parentis,—pray tell me what you think. But do not judge me by the activity of mind, which you and a few others possess, for in that case, the more different things in hand, the pleasanter the work; but, though I hope I never shall be idle, such is not the case with me.[2]

Ever dear H. Yrs most truly,

C. Darwin

[1] See footnote to Letter 31, p. 87.
[2] Four months later he accepted the secretaryship. He held the post from Feb. 16, 1838, till Feb. 19, 1841.

LETTER 55

[*To: The Revd Professor Henslow, Cambridge*
Post Paid. Postmark: PAID 4 NO 4 1837]

[*4 Nov 1837*]

My dear Henslow

Will you have the kindness to give a message to Prof. Miller from me, & another to L. Jenyns.—I write to you because I do not want to trouble either of them with a letter for a single word, —and you will probably soon see them & give it vivâ voce.—I left with Miller last winter some geological specimens.—I should be very much obliged if he would make [SOON *added*] a list of the numbers (*specifying the colour of the paper*), for otherwise I might be hunting in vain for hours. I ought at the time to have made a list, but neglected doing so. When I know which he has got, I will ask him to tell me something [about *added*] those which I may want, & which he had the kindness to say he would do.

My message to L. Jenyns is simply that I expect T. Eyton to pay me a visit before long, when he comes up to town, & that the fish had better be sent soon by waggon to 36 Great Marlborough St.—

Pray tell Leonard that my government work is going on smoothly & I hope will be prosperous.—He will see in the prospectus his name attached to the fish. I set my shoulder to the work with a good heart.—I am very much better than I was during the last month [of my *del*] before my Shrewsbury visit—I fear the geology will take me a great deal of time, I was looking over one set of notes, & the quantity I found I had to read, for that one place, was frightful.—If I live till I am eighty years old I shall not cease to marvel at finding myself an author: in the summer before I started, if anyone had told me I should have been an angel by this time, I should have thought it an equal improbability. This marvellous transformation is all owing to you.—I am sorry to find that a good many errata are left in the part [of *added*] my volume, which is printed: During my absence Mr. Colburn employed some goose to revise, & he has Multiplied instead of diminishing my oversights: but for all that the smooth paper and clear type has a charming appearance, and I sat the other evening gazing in silent admiration at the first page of my own volume, when I received it from the printers! Goodbye My dear Henslow—pray remember me to Mrs. Henslow and all your family, by whom I shall be quite forgotten, if I do not pay Cambridge a visit before very long; but when that is to be "Quien sabe?" as the Spaniard says.

C. Darwin

Saturday

LETTER 56

[To: The Revd Prof. Henslow, Cambridge
Double P.P.
Postmark: PAID 20No20 1837]

21 Nov 1837

My dear Henslow

Will you oblige me by looking over the enclosed *prospectus*.— My publisher has almost entirely altered the one I wrote; perhaps he has improved some parts, but I do not like others.—He has asked me to get someone to read it over.—The sentence written at the bottom, appears to me better than the three short printed ones.—Will you return it with any one of the proofs with any marginal observations on it.—My journal, I am very glad to be able to tell you, is very near its end.—One more chapter, & that not a very long one, will complete the task, which I fear must have been a heavier one, than you could have anticipated.—My journal, I suspect, will not be published for several months,—but it is a great satisfaction to me to feel my hands nearly clear for other work.—I am going tomorrow morning to the Isle of Wight & shall return on Wednesday night.—I heard yesterday from Fox, who told me he intended paying me a visit, as we have never seen each other since my return.—But as Fox is so delicate a person, I thought it a shame to allow him to travel in this cold weather, so I am going to anticipate him, though just at present

I can ill spare the time. I called on Mr. Spring Rice, about a fortnight since, to thank him for his very considerate kindness in
writing to me himself about the Grant.—As long as he remains
in office, I am sure I shall have no trouble from government. He
was congratulating himself, that the country might support *even
the misfortune* of having a whig ministry, when they were occasionally able to do such good acts as give you a living.—I never
saw a man look more pleased as he said so.—

I find London at this time of the year, most delightfully tran-
quil, especially as I never call on anyone.—Goodbye

Most truly yours
Chas. Darwin

Thank you for doing my servant's business. I forwarded Prof.
Don's parcel.

PART II

Letters 1838–60

LETTER 57

[*To: Professor Henslow*
No postmark]

36 Grt Marlbro' St
Monday.—[*26 March 1838*]

My dear Henslow

I am ashamed to trouble you with an answer, simply to say I cannot come, but as the invitation to the Ray dinner is formal I thought I ought to answer.—I am much obliged to Mr Peacock for his "*insi*nuation" & I should like to be with you very much, but I am tied firmly by the leg by the hundred and one details, I find I incur with my Editorship of the Zoology—Beagle's Voyage.—

I am moreover Goth enough to prefer paying you a quiet visit to meeting all the world at a great Dinner.—Many thanks for your last letter, which delights me touching the Journal.—You and others are magnificent in presenting my work to the Cambridge. Phil. Soc.—Will you tell Miller how much obliged I am to him for determining the mineral for me. But will you say, that the point I am most anxious about with re- gard to the specimen (378 yellow) is whether in those cells where there are two kinds of minerals,—one opake, & one crystallized,—whether *both* are Chabasie[1] as the point appears to me a cur[ious, *word half torn off*] one with respect to the formation of the crystallized mineral which I suppose is the Chabasie.—

Most truly ys.
Chas. Darwin

Monday.—
I am going out to dine with Lyell so am in a hurry.

[1] 'Chabazite, chabasite .. also chabasie. A blundered name, which ought to be Chalazite.' (*O.E.D.*) A colourless or flesh-coloured mineral occurring widely distributed, in glassy rhombohedral, almost cubic crystals, composed chiefly of silica, alumina and lime.

LETTER 58

[*Letter from Professor Henslow to Charles Darwin on his engagement, 1838. On the envelope in Mrs Litchfield's writing: 'Congrats on engage- mt hardly any good but pleasant & wise'. Mrs Litchfield, Darwin's daughter, probably wrote this note when looking through letters before publishing 'Emma Darwin, A Century of Family Letters', privately printed 1904, published by John Murray, 1915.*]

[*To: C. Darwin Esq, 36 Grt Marlborough St, London From: Professor J. S. Henslow*]

Cambridge
16 Dec 1838

My dear Darwin,—

This day 15 years ago I entered on that state which, it rejoices my pericardium to think that you are about to enter—I have been remiss in not telling you so sooner, but I am sure you will not think me unmindful of your happiness from having added one more specimen of my carelessness to the many you have witnessed before—All I can wish you is, that you may experience as great content in the marriage state as I have done myself—& all the advice, which I need not give you, is, to remember that as you take your wife for better for worse, be careful to value the better & care nothing for the worse—Of course it is impossible for a lover to suppose for an instant that there can be any worse in the matter, but it is the prudent part of a husband, to provide that there shall be none—It is the neglect of this little particular which makes the marriage state of so many men worse than their single blessedness—if there is such a thing—for it is now so long since I have enjoyed my double blessedness that I cannot fancy myself in my Bachelor days—One piece of more serious advice I shall just venture to hint at—that we do well to remember daily that our greatest earthly blessings may be taken from us in a moment. So far from this reflection annoying us & preventing our happi- ness from being as complete as earthly happiness can be—I have my own experience to assure you that it encreases happiness, & removes many an anxious mental care. But I am afraid you will

John Stevens Henslow, F.L.S., by T. H. Maguire, 1849

Charles Robert Darwin, F.R.S., by T. H. Maguire, 1849

think I am writing a sermon. Only take it in good part, & believe that I most heartily wish you all joy & prosperity—Is there a chance of your coming here this Xmas—Mrs. H. is anxious to know & bids me ask you—

Yr. ever affect^{ly}

J. S. Henslow

LETTER 59

[*To: Professor Henslow
No Postmark*]

26 Jan. 1840
Friday morning

My dear Henslow

I have just received your letter, as the waggon goes tomorrow, I pack up the specimens at once.—I believe you may keep them all.—They all come from the Maldeeve & Chagos lagoon—islands or atolls in the Indian Ocean.—islands precisely like Keeling Island.—

I hope they may be of any use to you.—I send a couple copy of abstract of my worm Paper[1] useless to me.—Of course you have thought of Drummonds light[2]—Also of the use put to burn coral, shells, & limestone in the East Indian Archipelago to give a relish to the chewing of Betel.—In S. America, I believe [caustic *del*] potash is used, in analogous manner in chewing the Cocos leaves.—

I am in a hurry so good Bye
C. Darwin

[1] 'On the Formation of Mould', *Geol. Soc. Proc.*, Vol. II, 1838, pp. 574–6; *Geol. Soc. Trans.*, Vol. V, 1840, pp. 505–10. Darwin's volume, *The Formation of Vegetable Mould, through the action of Worms, with Observations on their Habits*, was not published until 1881. The worm-stone, designed by Charles's son Horace, which was used for measuring the subsidence owing to the action of worms, is still to be seen (1967) in the garden at Down House in Kent.

[2] Thomas Drummond, R.E., 1797–1840; introduced 'Drummond' lime-light; improved heliostat. Head of Boundary Commission under Reform Bill, 1833; Under-Secretary for Ireland, 1835. Originated the saying: 'Prosperity has its duties as well as its rights.'

L

turn over [*on back of sheet*]
Do you recollect our discussion about varieties of [same *added*] plants not having *three* primary [colours *omitted*]—surely I have seen pale yellow hyacinth, & certainly blue and pink ones.—pray tell me is it not so.

LETTER 60

[*To: Professor Henslow*
No Postmark]

Shrewsbury
July 3rd 1840

My dear Henslow
I remember in your lecture you said *monsters* were sometimes curious.—We have a largish orange tree, covered with oranges & nearly all these are annually horned, that is they have two or four projections, covered with the yellow rind, like cows horns in shape. Many of the oranges are deeply ribbed, the number of ribs being generally seven, sometimes six or five.—It is evident the horns are the segments more perfectly separated.—I send a minute ribbed one, with one cow's horn.—These horns branch off sometimes near footstalk, sometimes near apex.—The little one does not look odd, the big oranges with the good large horns look very curious.—The tree has long been without manure.— If these are curious & exemplify the metamorphoses of some organ into the fruit orange, I will get a series. If not curious do NOT ANSWER this note. If you do care much about them let me know before next Tuesday when I return to Maer.—
Ever your's
C. Darwin

LETTER 61

[*To:Professor Henslow*
No postmark]

Sept 18th [*1842*]

My dear Henslow

I bequest to your Museum.—a parcel of Paints with wh. Fuegians colour their bodies. Two spears with which they spear Porpoises Fish, Otters & Guanaco, etc.—And a Pacific Dolphin's Hook.

Ever yours
C. Darwin

LETTER 62

[*To: Professor Henslow*
No postmark]

Saturday 8 Sept 1843
Down. Bromley
Kent

My dear Henslow

Lindley[1] tells me in a note that he has sent you an Atriplex to look at unknown to him—I do not know whether he has told you its interesting history and how worthy it is of careful examination. A Mr. W. Kemp, (an almost labouring Scotchman) who has occasionally corresponded with me on Geolog: topics, sent me a parcel of seeds, which he found [at *del*] in the bottom-layer of sand in a great sand-pit, many feet deep, near Melrose, & which sand-pit is now much above the level of the river & must have been deposited, when the features of the country were quite different & [when *del*] apparently before [the *del*] a barrier of rock was cut through & a lake drained.—He well says that no geologist will pretend to guess how many thousands & thousands

---

[1] Presumably John Lindley, 1799–1865. A distinguished taxonomic botanist and horticulturist; Professor of Botany in University of London, 1829–60; Assistant Secretary to the Horticultural Society, and helped to found the *Gardeners' Chronicle*. F.R.S., 1828. Author of *The Vegetable Kingdom*, 1846. Mainly responsible for saving Kew Gardens for the nation.

of years must have elapsed.—If he had not shown himself to me a most careful, & ingenious observer, I sh^d have thought nothing of the case. But he is positive the seeds were embedded with vegetable matter in a *layer* at the bottom of the sand, & separating it from gravel. Now if this Atriplex turns out new to England or a well marked new variety, it will really be like recovering an extinct creation.—He was going in the Spring to publish an account of this, but I persuaded him to wait till his plants had been examined. His seeds germinated freely, do you not think it w^d be worth while to send a specimen to Babington,[1]—that man of varieties—Do you chance to know where he is? I w^d send him one—Lindley in a note to me, speaks of some great discovery of a monster near Ely, showing that the nucleus of the ovule is [merely *del*] only another form of the *growing point*—Can you explain to me, what this means—it is a dead language to me— When you have made out the Atriplex, will you let me hear what you think, as I am curious myself & wait to communicate the result to Mr. Kemp.—With kind remembrances to Mrs Henslow

Ever yours
C. Darwin

LETTER 63

[*To: Professor Henslow*
No postmark]

14 Oct 1843
Saturday

Shrewsbury
(where I am come for a weeks visit)

My dear Henslow,

I fear you will be wearied about the Atriplex: I have written to Mr Kemp to ascertain what precautions he took in sowing his

[1] Charles Cardale Babington, 1808–95. Succeeded Henslow as Professor of Botany in Cambridge in 1861. One of the founders of the Entomological Society, 1833, and of the Ray Club in 1836. F.R.S., 1851. Works include *Manual of British Botany*, 1843 (ten editions to 1922); *Flora of Cambridgeshire*, 1861; and *The British Rubi*, 1869.

seeds.—But do you not think that the same odd variety of the Atriplex, having come up in the Hort. Soc & at Mr Kemps, shows that as far as this one species is concerned, there can be no doubt? It will be rather *flat*, if you ultimately pronounce the Atriplex to be merely a variety, although one new to you.—I was mentioning the last week the case to E. Forbes[1] & he suggested (what I had thought of, but had forgotten) my sending a specimen to Babington, that mighty man for minute differences of British Plants. I think I will [do so *partly obliterated*] as anyhow it w^d. be worth hearing what he thinks. I am full of surprise at your new trade & the success you have met with in *modelling*—300 people must have paid their shilling fee!

Ever yours
C. D.—

LETTER 64

[*To: Professor Henslow*
No postmark]

Down Bromley Kent
Saturday 5 Nov. 1843

My dear Henslow

I sent that weariful Atriplex to Babington, as I said I would, & he tells me that he has reared a fac-simile by sowing the seed of A. angustifolia (I see Hooker considers the angustifolia is a variety of A. patula) [*added between lines*] in rich soil.—He says he knows the A. hastata & that it is very different.—Until your last note I had not heard that Mr Kemp's seeds had produced two Polygonums. He informs me he saw each plant bring up the husk of the individual seed which he planted—I believe myself in his accuracy, but I have written to advise him not to publish, for as he [sowed *del*] collected only two kinds of seed—& from them

---

[1] Edward Forbes, 1815–54. Naturalist, palaeontologist and geologist. Lecturer of the Geological Society, 1842; Professor of Botany at King's College, London, 1843. Wrote *History of British Mollusca*, 1848; *History of British Star-fishes*, 1842, besides many scientific papers. See *Autobiography*, p. 125; and *LL*, II, p. 38.

2. Polygonums. 2. spec. or var. of Atriplex & a Rumex have come up, anyone w^d say (as you suggested) that more probably all the seeds were in the soil, than that seeds, which must have been buried for tens of thousands of years, sh^d retain their vitality —If the Atriplex had turned out new, the evidence would indeed have been good.—I regret this result of poor Mr Kemps seeds, especially as I believe from his statements and the appearance of the seeds, that they did germinate & I further have no doubt that their antiquity must be immense.[1]—I am sorry also for the trouble you have had—I heard the other day through a circuitous course, how you are astonishing all the clodhoppers in your whole part of the country & far more wonderful, as it was remarked to me, that you had not in doing this aroused the envy of all the good surrounding sleeping parsons—what good you must do to the present & all succeeding generations.—Farewell, my dear patron.

CD

LETTER 65

[*C.U.L. from a copy*]
[*To: Prof. Henslow*
From: C. Darwin]

Down, Bromley, Kent.
Friday 25 July 1845

My dear Henslow.

Very many thanks for your ten notes and enclosures; I had seen the Paragraph otherwise I should have been much interested in the death of (as he styled himself) "Comte Thierry, King of

---

[1] Darwin continued to take a lively interest in the longevity of seeds, and on the result of their immersion in sea-water. He wrote six papers on the subject in the *Gardeners' Chronicle and Agricultural Gazette* in 1855. See also *LL*, II, p. 65, wherein a letter to J. D. Hooker, 1855, he wrote of a case told him by a man, which he at first thought splendid, adding: 'and *splendid* it was, for according to his evidence the seed came up alive out of the *lower* part of the *London Clay*!!! I disgusted him by telling him that Palms ought to have come up.'

Nukahiva and Sovereign Chief of New Zealand". I wonder what has become of his wretched wife. I sincerely hope that your allotments will succeed; all that I have read in favour of them sounds most encouraging, and I have never been convinced by what has been written against them. I have bought a Farm in Lincolnshire and when I go there this Autumn, I mean to see what I can do in providing any cottage on my small estate with gardens—It is a hopeless thing to look to but I believe few things would do this Country more good in future ages than the destruction of primogeniture,—so as to lessen the difference in land wealth and make more small freeholders. How atrociously unjust are the stamp laws which render it so expensive for the poor man to buy his $\frac{1}{4}$ of an acre, it makes one's blood burn with indignation. Have you seen Lyells Travels? He says the poorer classes in Canada complain of the lumber duties! so that our Cottages are badly built under pretence of benefiting a few rich merchants, really no doubt for our own landowners.

Thanks for the slip about the Crag—I am astonished that stones containing 50–60 per cent of Phosphate of Lime are not most valuable.

A fortnight ago we had born a little boy, our fourth child.— He is to be called George; & I believe I have pleasant associations with that name from formerly playing with your Boy.—I hope Mrs. Henslow is better.

Farewell.
C.D.

LETTER 66

[*This letter was brought back to me from the American Philosophical Society, Philadelphia, in August 1963 by Dr Sydney Smith. It is typed on a half-sheet, with some copyist's errors, probably a dealer's copy when offering it for sale. The location of the original is not known. I felt it well worth including in the series, with the vivid relevance to the Hungry Forties, and the Corn Laws.*]

[*To: The Rev^d. Professor Henslow, Cambridge*]

Down, Bromley, Kent
Oct. 28th 1845

My dear Henslow

I have to thank you for several printed notices about the potatoes etc etc. What a painfully interesting subject it is: I have just returned home and have looked over my potatoes and find the crop small, a good many having rotted in the ground, but the rest well.[1]—I am drying sand today in the oven to store with the greatest care in baskets my seed-potatoes. I think it a very good suggestion of yours, about gentlefolk not buying potatoes, and I will follow it for one. The poor people, wherever I have been, seem to be in great alarm: my laborer here has not above a few weeks consumption and those not sound; as he complains to me, it is a dreadful addition to the evil, flour being so dear: some time ago this same man told me, that when flour rose, his family consumed 15 pence more of his 12s earnings per week on this one article. This would be nearly as bad as if for one of us we had to pay an additional 50 or 100£ for our bread: how soon in that case would those infamous corn laws be swept away.

At Shrewsbury we tryed the potato flour: how very curiously soon the starch separates; it really is quite a pretty experiment. I

---

[1] J. C. Drummond in *The Englishman's Food*, 1939, wrote: 'Things came to a head in 1845 when, with wages at the lowest level they had touched for over a century, the food situation became desperate for the very poor as a result of a widespread invasion of "potatoe disease" in conjunction with a poor corn harvest. England has never been nearer to revolution. The microscopic fungus (*phytophthora infestans*), however, did what twenty years of bitter agitation had failed to do; it brought about the repeal of the Corn Laws in 1846.'

have been taking a little time, primarily to see a farm which I have purchased in Lincolnshire[1] as an investment (and on which I have told my agent to arrange allotments for every laborer) and then I went and saw Yorke and visited the Dean of Manchester, and had some hours talk—I then visited Mr. Waterton at Walton Hall, and was exceedingly amused with my visit, and with the man; he is the strangest mixture of extreme kindness, harshness and bigotry, that I ever saw.—Finally I visited Chatsworth, with which I was, like a child, transported with delight.—Have you ever seen it? Really the great Hothouse, and especially the water part, is more wonderfully like tropical nature, than I could have conceived possible.—Art beats Nature altogether there.

I have been most sincerely grieved at Hoskins disappointment at Edinburgh: I cannot but think he will make a great Botanist; it is admirable what a stock of general and accurate knowledge he appears to have on all such subjects, as geographical range, etc, etc.

We are all flourishing here with the exception of my weariful stomach.—I hope Mrs. Henslow is better: pray remember me very kindly to her.

> Ever my dear Henslow
> Yours truly
> C. Darwin

LETTER 67

[*To: Professor Henslow*
No postmark]

> Down Farnborough Kent
> 6 October 1846.
> Monday Morning

My dear Henslow
In a few day's time my third & last Part of the *Geology of the Voyage of the Beagle*,[2] viz on S. America will be published, & I

[1] With regard to Darwin's Lincolnshire farm see *LL*, I, p. 343, in letter to C. Lyell.
[2] *Geological Observations on South America*. Being the third part of the *Geology of the Voyage of the 'Beagle'*, 1846. See Bibliography, p. 218.

want to know how I can send you a copy. I take shame to myself that the others were not sent, for I consider that you have a *right* to them. Have you any house of call, where your parcels accumulate? I am very sorry & so is my wife that your scheme of paying us, a little visit on your way to Mr Jenyns broke down. – I sh^d. have much enjoyed having you here. I was at Southampton[1] & saw there L. Jenyns: I did not think he was looking at all well; sadly too thin: I was very glad to hear from him, that Mrs Henslow was a little better. L. Jenyns new book appears a very nice one, as far as I have read.—I wish you had been at Southampton; there was a capital congregation of naturalists & I saw many old friends & was introduced to many new acquaintances. Altogether we enjoyed (for my wife was with me) our week exceedingly, & took some little excursions, especially one to Winchester Cathedral. I think I shall certainly attend the Oxford meeting & no doubt you will be there. You cannot think how delighted I feel at having finished all my Beagle materials, except some invertebrata: it is now 10 years since my return, & your words, which I thought preposterous, are come true, that it w^d take twice the number of years to describe, that it took to collect & observe. Farewell my dear Henslow, how I wish that I lived nearer to you

Yours most truly
C. Darwin

LETTER 68

[To: Professor Henslow, Hitcham Rectory, Hadleigh, Suffolk.
Postmarks: DOWN BROMLEY AP2 B S 3 AP 3 1848.

HADLEIGH AP 4 1848]

Down Farnborough Kent
Saturday night 1 April 1848

My dear Henslow
Thank you for your note & giving me a chance of seeing you in town; but it was out of my power to take advantage of it, for I

---

[1] Meeting of the British Association; President, Sir Roderick Murchison, Bt., K.C.B., F.R.S.

had previously arranged to go up to London on Monday. I should have much enjoyed seeing you. Thanks, also, for your Address,[1] which I like very much. The anecdote about Whewell[2] & the tides, I had utterly forgotten; I believe it is near enough to the truth.—I rather demur to one sentence of yours, viz "however delightful any scientific pursuit may be, yet if it shall be wholly unapplied it is of no more use than building castles in the air". Would not your hearers infer from this that the practical use of each scientific discovery ought to be immediate and obvious to make it worthy of admiration? What a beautiful instance Chloroform is of a discovery made from *purely* scientific researches, afterwards coming almost by chance into practical use. For myself I would, however, take higher ground, for I believe there exists, & I feel within me, an instinct for truth; or knowledge or discovery, of something [of the *added*] same nature as the instinct of virtue, & that our having such an instinct is reason enough for scientific researches without any practical results *ever* ensuing from them.—You will wonder what makes me run on so, but I have been working very hard for the last 18 months on the anatomy etc of the Cirripedia (on which I shall publish a monograph) & some of my friends laugh at me, & I fear the study of the cirripedia will ever remain "wholly unapplied" & yet I feel that such study is better than castle-building.[3] Talking of

[1] Given in the Ipswich Museum in March, 1848, soon after it was opened, to the Ipswich Society. The Rev. W. Kirby was the first President, to be succeeded by the Rev. J. S. Henslow in 1850. The subscribers' aim was in line with the current movement for 'giving Instruction to the Working Classes in various branches of Science, and more especially in Natural History'. But Henslow threw his net over a wider audience, and alludes to 'those gross blunders which are so constantly made, even by otherwise well-educated persons, concerning the nature and origin of many of the natural objects with which we are daily familiar'. The address was never printed, except for extracts in L. Jenyns's *Life of the Rev. J. S. Henslow*, 1862; see pp. 150-4. At Henslow's installation as President in December 1850, Edward Forbes went down to Ipswich to give a gratis lecture, and wrote: 'I stayed with Ransome, who gave a great dinner party . . . when it was pleasant to see the bishop, four or five clergymen, and a bushel of naturalists, all dining at the table of a quaker chemist and druggist.' See *Memoir of Edward Forbes* by G. Wilson and A. Geikie, pp. 281-2.

[2] See footnote to Letter 31, p. 87.

[3] Darwin's work on the *Cirripedia* (barnacles) occupied eight years of his life, 1846-54. He sometimes wondered whether the expenditure of so much time had

Cirripedia, I must tell you a curious case I have just these few last days made out: all the Cirripedia are bisexual, except one genus, & in this the female has the ordinary appearance, whereas the male has no one part of its body like the female & is microscopically minute; but here comes the odd fact, the male or sometimes two males, at the instant they cease being locomotive larvae become parasitic within the sack of the female, & [have *del*] thus fixed [& half embedded in the flesh of their wives *added*] they pass their whole lives and can never move again. Is it not strange that nature should have made this one genus unisexual, & yet have fixed the males on the outside of the females;—the male organs in fact being thus external instead of internal.—I am delighted to hear good accounts of Hooker:[1] If he should write to *you* any letter which might be forwarded, I should be very glad to see it: I seldom hear any news of him, as I am so little in town, & never see Sir W. Hooker. I do hope his great undertaking will well answer to him.—Pray remember me very kindly to Mrs & Miss Henslow. How pleasant the meeting at Oxford was;[2] it is a white week in my memory. We are all well here, & a sixth little (d)[3] expected this summer: as for myself, however,

---

been worth while. But the detailed physiological insight he acquired was a lasting asset, and an essential foundation for his future theories. See Appendix 2 and Bibliography.

[1] Joseph Hooker, 1817–1911, botanist and traveller, who later became Darwin's closest personal and botanical friend; married Henslow's daughter Frances in 1851. At the date of this letter, 1848, he was engaged on his travels in India, undertaken with the help of a Government grant and a free passage on the Governor General's ship; he left England in November 1847. See his *Himalayan Journal*, 2 vols., 1854. He followed his father, Sir William Hooker, as Director of Kew Gardens in 1865. Writer of many botanical works, including the six-volume results of the botanical work of his first voyage with Sir J. C. Ross's Antarctic expedition, 1839–43, published 1844–60; and the *Essay on the Flora of Tasmania*, 1860, when he was one of the first to use Darwin's and Wallace's Natural Selection theory as a working hypothesis for descent with modification. Also *Handbook of New Zealand Flora*, and *Flora of the British Isles*, and many other publications. See also Letters 70, 71, 73 and 74.

[2] The British Association met in Oxford in 1847, under the Presidency of Sir Robert Inglis, Bt., M.P., F.R.S.

[3] 'little (d)' again occurs in later letters, and probably stands either for 'darwin' or 'descendant'.

I have had more unwellness than usual. Believe me, my dear Henslow.

Ever most truly yours
C. Darwin

If you are ever starting any young naturalist with his tools, recommend him to go to Smith & Beck of 6 Colman St. City for a simple microscope: he has lately made one for me, partly from my own model and with hints from Hooker, *wonderfully* superior for coarse and fine definitions than any I ever before worked with. If I had had it sooner, it would have saved me many an hour.—

LETTER 69

[*To: Professor Henslow*
No Postmark]

Down Farnborough Kent
July 2ᵈ [*1848*]

My dear Henslow

I am uncommonly sorry to hear so poor an account of several members of your family; but I do hope that the sea will do all good. Nothing comes up to the misery of having illness amongst one's children, of which we have [lately *added*] had a touch, now happily quite over.—We expect a sixth (d) in beginning of August. Thanks for your Syllabus, which I shall be curious to look over. I never *enjoyed* any other lectures in my life, except yours, for Edinburgh completely sickened me of that method of learning. What a grand step it would be to break down the system of eternal classics & nothing but classics.—I am perfectly certain, that the only thing at Cambridge which did my mind any good, were your lectures & still more your conversation; I believe I must except, also, getting up Paley's Evidences. It would indeed, be a grand step to get a little more diversity in study for men of different minds. Talking of classics reminds me to ask you to do me a very *essential* favour:[1] I find I have utterly forgotten my

---

[1] There is much underlining besides the words *enjoyed* and *essential* in this letter, which I have omitted in the belief that it is not in Darwin's hand.

whole immense stock of classical knowledge which put me in the eminent position of 5th or 6th in the hoi polloi.[1]

Now I have to invent many names of families & genera for my work on Cirripedia, & I have not the SMALLEST idea whether my names are correct. W^{d}. you let me send them to you, for your opinion from [life *del*] time to time? My paper c^{d} be returned with your fiat, so that you w^{d} have but little writing, or indeed hardly any.—

When you are walking on the shore, w^{d} you take the trouble to scrape me off (taking care to get the base) a few Barnacles, of as many different forms as *you* can see, & send them me in a little [strong *added*] box, damp with seaweed. I am anxious to make out the distribution of the British species—And new species may turn up, for the group has [not *del*] been made out most superficially,—for instance under Balanus punctatus (which must be made a distinct genus) three or four varieties have been called distinct species; whereas one form, which has not been called even a variety, is not only a distinct genus, but a distinct subfamily.—Yesterday I found four [or 5 *added*, distinct *del*] named genera are all the closest species of one genus: this will give you a specimen of the utter confusion my poor dear Barnacles are in.—I am in a very cock-a-hoop state about my anatomy of the Cirripedia, & think I have made out some very curious points; my Book will be published in two years by the Ray Soc.[2] & will I trust do no discredit (see how vain I am!) to your old pupil & most attached friend

C. Darwin

[The Traveller, *added in another hand*]

---

[1] Actually he was tenth.

[2] *A Monograph of the Sub-class Cirripedia*, with Figures of all the Species. The Lepadidae or Pedunculated Cirripedes. 1851 (Ray Society). Also *The Balanidae* (or Sessile Cirripedes) etc. 1854 (Ray Society).

LETTER 70

[*To: Rev. Prof. Henslow*
From: C. Darwin]

The Lodge, Malvern
May 6, 1849

My dear Henslow

Your kind note has been forwarded to me here. You will be surprised to hear that we all, children servants and all have been here for nearly two months. All last autumn and winter my health grew worse and worse; incessant sickness, tremulous hands and swimming head; I thought I was going the way of all flesh. Having heard of much success in some cases from the Cold Water Cure, I determined to give up all attempts to do anything and come here and put myself under Dr. Gully. It has answered to a considerable extent: my sickness much checked and considerable strength gained. Dr. G., moreover, (and I hear he rarely speaks confidently) tells me he has little doubt but that he can cure me, in the course of time, time however it will take. l have experienced enough to feel sure that the Cold Water Cure is a great powerful agent and upsetter of all constitutional habits. Talking of habits the cruel wretch has made me leave off snuff—that chief solace of life. We thank you most sincerely for your prompt and early invitation to Hitcham for Brit. Assoc. for 1850: if I am made well and strong, *most* gladly will I accept it; but as I have been hitherto, a drive every day of half-a-dozen miles would be more than I could stand with attending any of the sections. I intend going to Birmingham, if able; indeed I am bound to attempt it, for I am honoured beyond all measure in being one of the V.P.[1] I am uncommonly glad you will be there; I fear, however, we shall not have any such charming trips as Nuneham and Dropmore. We shall stay here till at least June 1st, perhaps till July 1st., and I shall have to go on with the aqueous treatment at home for several more months. One most singular effect of the treatment is, that it induces in most people, and eminently in my case, the most

[1] Vice-President of the British Association.

complete stagnation of mind; I have ceased to think even of
Barnacles!

I heard sometime since from Hooker; but the letter was so purely
Geological that I did not suppose it would interest Miss Henslow:[1]
How capitally he seems to have succeeded in all his enterprises.
You must be very busy now: I happened to be thinking the other
day over the Gamlingay trip to the Lilies of the Valley: are [*ah!*]
those were delightful days when one had no such organ as a
stomach, only a mouth and the masticating appurtenances.

I am very much surprised at what you say, that men are beginning to work in earnest the [*at?*] Botany. What a loss it will be
for Nat. History that you have ceased to reside all the year in
Cambridge. My dear Henslow farewell.

Yours most affectionately
C. Darwin

I hope that Mrs. Henslow is much better; we are all flourishing.

LETTER 71

[*To: Professor Henslow*
No postmark]

Down Farnborough Kent
Wednesday [After Sept.
21, 1849, when Darwin
returned from Birmingham]

My dear Henslow

It was a great disappointment to us not finding you at Birmingham—[2] I looked many times in vain to the letter H. in the
alphabetical list during the first two days, & then gave you up;
fearing that Sunday was to blame. Both my wife & self had
looked forward to meeting you, as one of our greatest pleasures.
Fox, also, disappointed us. It was a good meeting, but partly
from not being very well & partly from the place being so

---

[1] Later to become Joseph Hooker's wife.
[2] Meeting of British Association, President Rev. T. R. Robinson, F.R.S.

large & nasty, the meeting was not very brilliant to me,—not to be put into same class with the Oxford Meeting, which, however, was too pleasant to be hoped to be rivalled. What days were Blenheim, Nuneham & especially Dropmore! We started for Warwick & Kenilworth, but I broke down & became so unwell, I had to stop at Leamington. I go on with the Water Cure very steadily & keep on deriving considerable benefit from it, as long as I live the regular life of a hermit, but I think I stand any change, even worse than formerly & my stomach has not got over the excitement of Birmingham as yet.— Your Allotment scheme seems an excellent one: how active you always seem to be with your many plans of doing good to your Parish.—Pray remember me very kindly to Mrs Henslow & to Miss Henslow; ask her, when she next writes to Hooker to send him my kindest remembrances & say I do not write, having nothing to communicate—ex nihilo nihil fit, & as I see nobody & hear nothing I have nothing to write about. I heartily wish he was home again.—I travelled down to Birmingham with Col. Sabine[1] his wife & her mother & I found them as ardent admirers of Hooker as I c^d. desire. Mrs. Sabine & I agreed too perfectly over the capital powers of description shown in Hooker's letters from the Erebus; [but *del*] if he will [but *added*] write as well from India, what a capital book he will make.—

Talking about books, what praise you give me; but do you not know that it is very conceited in you to praise me, for assuredly you more than half formed my mind, you in fact are giving yourself half of a very pleasant dish of praise.—I have heard nothing of Leonard Jenyns for an age: I hope he is well; I had expected also to meet him at Birmingham & was disappointed.

Your most truly
C. Darwin

[1] General Sir Edward Sabine, 1788–1883, astronomer and physicist. One of the secretaries to the Royal Society, 1829; scientific adviser to Admiralty; Secretary to British Association 1839–59.

It was in General Sabine's Presidential Address to the Royal Society in 1864, presenting the Copley Medal to Charles Darwin, that he spoke rashly in the name of the Society after discussing *O* with cautious praise, concluding: 'Speaking

M

LETTER 72

[To: Professor Henslow
No postmark]

Down Farnborough Kent
Jan 17th [*1850*]

My dear Henslow

Mr Ransome[1] has in the most magnificent manner, & owing he says to all that he has heard you say of me, presented me with a complete series of the Ipswich likenesses. In consequence I have you in duplicate & wish therefore to return one copy to you.— Will you tell me where I can have it left for you in London.—I have some copies of my own likeness, which you no doubt have in the series, otherwise I sh^d of course have been proud to have sent you one.—My wife says she never saw me with the smile, as engraved, but that otherwise it is very like.—my said wife has been occupied these two days past in producing a fourth boy Darwin & seventh child! He is to be called Leonard,—a name I hold in affection from Cambridge & other associations.—I was so bold during my wifes confinement which are always rapid, as to administer Chloroform, before the Dr came & I kept her in a state of insensibility of 1 & $\frac{1}{2}$ hours & she knew nothing from first pain till she heard that the child was born.—It is the greatest & most blessed of discoveries.

Yours affect
C. Darwin

I hope Mrs & Miss Henslow are well

[Added at side of letter]
I am at work again & believe I have succeeded in persuading our Clodhoppers to be enrolled in a Club.—

---

generally and collectively, we have expressly omitted it from the grounds of our award'. This caused great indignation amongst some members, and T. H. Huxley got the offending passage modified.

[1] The family of Ransome was active in the promotion of agricultural implements in Ipswich from 1779.

LETTER 73

[*To: Professor Henslow*
No postmark]

[*1850/51?*]
Down Farnborough Kent
Monday

My dear Henslow

I am extremely much obliged to you for your long letter on Benefit Clubs, which appears to me full of the *most* valuable suggestions. I have just sent it off to Mr Innes.[1]—Possibly either he or I may have to trouble you with a few further queries, but I hope not. The rules sent are considerably different from some of our adjoining clubs. Many thanks also for the fossil cirripedes— which I am VERY glad to have, as I can now open & break as many as I require: do not be insulted at my returning the postage of the parcel.—I really do not know who can help you with regard to secondary fossils, but I will not forget your wish.—I was ungrateful not to have thanked you for your Engraving, which I value much & shall have framed: it is very like, but I am not quite satisfied with it; I like in some respects the Photograph better.—I enclose a letter just received from Hooker; I fear the greater part will be too Geolog. for Miss Henslow but she will probably like to see parts of it.—When she returns it to me, will she be so good as to tell me how I ought to address a letter to him.—His thanks for my dull & few letters, I have most truly felt like burning coals on my head: my conscience acquits me of

---

[1] The Rev. J. Brodie Innes, Vicar of Down from 1846, wrote a warm tribute to Charles Darwin for inclusion in the biography, which his son was preparing in 1882, after his father's death; see *LL*, Vol. I, p. 143. He wrote: 'On my becoming Vicar of Down in 1846, we became friends, and so continued till his death. In all parish matters he was an active assistant; in matters connected with the schools, charities and other business, his liberal contribution was ever ready.'

For further information on Darwin's intimacy with the Vicar of Down, and his high opinion of his integrity, see 'The Darwin–Innes Letters, The Correspondence of an Evolutionist with his Vicar', *Annals of Science*, Vol. 17, No. 4, Dec. 1961, by Robert M. Stecher, M.D., of Cleveland, Ohio, U.S.A.

forgetting him, but it makes me feel very guilty of idleness &
stupidity.

Your most truly obliged

C. Darwin

LETTER 74

[*To: Professor Henslow*
No postmark]

[*1850/51?*]

My dear Henslow

Pray keep Hooker's letter as long as you like, & send it, if you
please, to Sir William.—Just look it over & see whether there is
not some expression about his Father being angry, which might
not be proper to send.—I remember in former letter his saying
that he had not told his Father how ill Falconer had behaved, as
it w^d have vexed him.—Mr. Innes, our clergyman, is greatly
obliged for your most valuable letter.—

In Haste

Yours most sincerely

C. Darwin

Your observation on Chalk flint strikes me as very curious.

LETTER 75

[*To: Professor Henslow*
No postmark]

Down Farnborough Kent

March 8th [*1853*]

My dear Henslow,

I am extremely much obliged to you for writing to Mr.
Warren:[1] I this morning heard from him from Brighton: *a very*

---

[1] I have not been able to find out about Mr Warren or the Company. Presumably this was one of Darwin's investments. See Sir Arthur Keith's *Darwin
Revalued*, 1955, Chap. 18, pp. 221 et seq.

obliging note, telling me he believes that everything is going on quite rightly with the Company: & that a friend of his, "a man high in the law" is a shareholder, who lives in London, & will etc all right. This is extremely satisfactory to me. My apprehension the [*that*] there was nothing to keep the Company any longer together, & therefore no security for my money must be ground- less.—I am really ashamed to think what trouble I have given you in regard to this Company. It has been my first, & certainly it shall be my last speculation. You shall have no more trouble on this head: & I hardly know anyone excepting yourself whom I could have troubled as I have done.—

I have copied the dates when you will be in London, and if I have to go up at all near those dates, I will write to Hooker, & find out your movements, & where I could see you. My wife & I *often* say that one of the very few things we regret, in having left London, is losing your visits.—I am astonished at the Snow having been so deep as to keep you from Ipswich: I am glad that the meeting went off so well.—

I sent £1. 1s. 0. to G. Ransome, when he applied to me sometime since; & I did not intend to give any more; but if you find so small an addition as another guinea, will make any difference, you can at any time put my name down for that: I fear you will think me rather shabby but there are plenty of local calls for money, I find, & I presume everyone finds it so.

My dear Henslow
Most truly yours
Charles Darwin

I have of course written to Mr. Warren & told him I w^d. inform you that he had written to me.

LETTER 76

[*To: Professor Henslow*
No postmark]

> Down Farnborough Kent
> March 31 [? *1853*]

My dear Henslow,
I am going to London for a few days on Monday, & should so very much like to see you, were it only for five minutes, on Wednesday, when you pass through London, I hope you will send me a line to my Brother's "57 Queen Anne St Cavendish Sq^{re}" to tell me whether you could arrange to meet me,—where & at what hour. Would it suit you to come to my Brothers to luncheon, at any hour you chose? it is a good central situation.

> Most truly yours
> Charles Darwin

LETTER 77

[*To: Professor Henslow*
No postmark]

> Down Farnborough Kent
> Dec. 11th [*1853?*]
> [*written on black edged paper*]

My dear Henslow
I am very much obliged for your note & the direction of the Pyrotechnist. Hearing all the things you do for your Parish, I am not at all surprised that you have discontinued the Fireworks;[1]— You formerly asked me for specimens for Ipswich, I have consequently packed up 20 to 25 specimens of Cirripedia of the several leading genera, & have named them: I have chiefly selected British species. They possess little value, excepting from being correctly named. In a few week's time, my volume by the

---

[1] L. Jenyns' *Memoir* of Henslow, p. 71. 'He had an annual exhibition of fireworks, which his knowledge of chemistry enabled him to let off on the rectory lawn, and which have always a great attraction with the lower orders.'

Ray Soc.[1] will be published, & I can *then* send you proofs of my Ten Plates, if worth having. I wish I could offer anything better to the Ipswich Soc[y]. but I have long ago distributed my collections. I am sorry to trouble you but will you tell me whether you or the Ipswich Mus: have any place of call in London to which I c[d]. address my parcel, carriage paid, or shall I send it direct to Ipswich or to you?—At the same time, will you tell me, (& it is the most important of my queries on Fire Works) *what sum of money will procure a fair village display?*

Now that my children are growing up & I think of educational processes, I often reflect over your inimitably (as it appears to me) good plan of teaching correct, concise language & accurate observation, namely by making your pupils describe leaves etc. I never profited myself by this, but very often [I have *added*] wished I had. Has it ever occurred to you, (I have often wished for something of the kind) that a most useful volume might be published, with woodcut outlines, & on separate pages well-weighed, concise descriptions in Saxon, & not scientific English. What a habit it would give to youths of thinking of the meaning of words, & what powers of expressing themselves! Compare such habits with [that of making *added*] wretched Latin verses. I did not intend to write so much; but it is an old wish of mine, that you or someone would undertake such a task.

My dear Henslow
Yours most truly
C. Darwin

I have no ideas on the arrangement of Museums, never having at all attended to the subject.

[1] The second Cirripede volume.

LETTER 78[1]

[*To: The Reverend Professor Henslow*
No postmark]

Down Farnborough Kent
Nov. 17 [*1854*]

My dear Henslow:

The next time you go to Ipswich to meet Dr. Clarke, the Editor of the Voyage of the Favourite, which was dedicated to you, I want you much to ask Dr. Clarke to ask the Sailor-author (I forget his name this minute) whether he has a *distinct* remembrance of having seen at Kerguelen Land, any drift sticks or timber thrown up by the sea.—

Please observe I do not want you to take the trouble to write about it,—any time [*?wd*] do for me. The reason I want to know is because Hooker's case of the several Kerguelen I. plants identical or closely allied to those of T. del Fuego, strikes me as the greatest anomaly known in the distribution of beings over the whole world, and therefore I am very curious to know, whether there is any conceivable (however improbable) means of their introduction by sea-currents.—

With this object, I know you will forgive me troubling you.—

I was exceedingly glad to hear a pretty good account of you from the Hookers who were here a short time since, and whose visit we enjoyed extremely.

Most truly yours,
C. Darwin

[1] This letter, written at a time when Darwin was investigating the possible transportation of plants over long distances by sea-currents, was brought to my notice by Dr Sydney Smith. The letter is in the possession of the American Philosophical Society, and the Librarian has allowed me to insert it in this collection. See *O*, sixth edition, pp. 341 and 355, where icebergs, as suggested by Lyell, are given as the possible means of dispersal.

LETTER 79

[*To: Professor Henslow*
No postmark]

Down March 13th/55

My dear Henslow
Many thanks for the list, & I shall be very glad to get the new edition. I am sorry that I have given you any trouble now that you are so very busy. I write to beg you not to think of the Anacharis[1] till you are *quite at leisure.*—
I will send the cirripedes next week to care of Mr. Webb.

Yours most truly
C. Darwin

LETTER 80

[*To: Professor Henslow*
No postmark]

Down Farnborough Kent
March 26th 1855

My dear Henslow
I found on my return home the Anarcharis, put by my wife in water & all flourishing for which very many thanks, & for which, as you are not a man to be offended, I send the 14 pennies, as by doing so I feel a honester man, & you will be by 14 pennies a richer man, & therefore according to Sydney Smith's high morality by exactly that much, a happier man, & according to City authorities, a *better* man. I saw Mr. Gosse[2] the other night & he told me that he had now the *same* several sea-animals [&

---

[1] *Anacharis* and *Anarcharis*, the former is the correct spelling. Nowadays referred to as *Elodea* (*E. canadinsis* Michx.)—N. Y. S.

[2] Philip Henry Gosse, 1810–88, naturalist, author of *A Naturalist's Rambles on the Devonshire Coast*, 1853; *Ompholos*, 1857, and other works. Although he accepted the literal interpretation of the Old Testament, he did much to encourage the knowledge of natural history. He introduced the aquarium for private use. See his son, Edmund Gosse's, *Life of Philip Henry Gosse*, 1890; and *Father and Son*, 1907.

algae *added*] living & breeding for 13 months in the *same* ARTI-
FICIALLY made sea water! Does not this tempt you? it almost
tempts me to set up a marine vivarium.—Remember in due time
the second edit of your Hitcham Flora, &, shᵈ. you ever stumble
on it, the fact on wild-geese.—I saw when in London Arch-
deacon Clive, & he most particularly enquired about you &
expressed a very strong wish to see you.—

My dear Henslow
Your affectionate old Pupil
C.D.

LETTER 81

[*To: Professor Henslow*
No postmark]

Down Farnborough Kent
June 27th 1855

My dear Henslow,
Very many thanks for the sermon & list of Plants, which though
no Botanist I have been very glad to see, to get some idea of
number of plants in a definite area. Though I modestly say I am
no Botanist, I am in fact a very celebrated one, for I have just
begun grasses & made out 28 species!!! which I consider a
wonderful triumph.—I return circular on account of misprint:
you have done me & my Barnacles much honour. And now try &
be very patient for I have a heap of favours to beg. I am really
anxious to know (but will not take up your time by detailing my
reasons) whether, you consider Lychnis diurna & L. vespertina
species or varieties: [their names are used by Gaertner on Hybrids:
added] am I right in considering L. diurna = L. sylvestris; & L.
vespertina = dioica? Judging from your own Cambridge list, I
infer you consider them as only varieties: the London Catalogue
& Babington consider them as species. If you consider them vars.
will you tell me on what grounds? Secondly: I have become very
fond of little experiments, & I mean to try whether I cannot break
the constitution of plants by coloured glass [picking off flowers,

sowing at wrong time etc *added*] etc etc etc in a short time; & I
want to know whether you can suggest any 2 or 3 hardy good
seeders, which you think from presenting doubtful forms, would
be interesting to try. Thirdly. Does Geum rivale or Epilobium
tetragonum grow in your neighbourhood (I do not believe either
are found here, on account of our dryness) & if they do grow,
would you take trouble to send me a dozen of the *finest* heads of
each, when nearly ripe, (but not so ripe as to shed seeds) that I
may count how many seeds each has for its maximum number, to
compare with some very prolific hybrids, which Dr. I. Bell Salter
is going to send me.—*Lastly*: busy as you are, can you forgive
these several requests?—I fear I am not a little unreasonable—I
want to know whether you would & this is the most troublesome
job, (though I think it sounds more troublesome than it is) sometime, say in winter [or whenever you have most Leisure *added*]
read over the names in the London Catalogue of Plants & I w^d
send my copy) pencil in Hand, & mark with cross, *all* those
species, which you believe to be [really *added*] species, but which
are *close* species;—taking some such definition for a "*close species*",
as a form, which even to a [good *added*] Botanist is a little troublesome to distinguish, or which you can just conceive possible,
though not probable, that further research will prove only to be
varieties. I am really very anxious for this, but I cannot explain
my motive, otherwise it might unconsciously to you influence the
result.[1] I do not think it would take up [much *added*] more time
than [going *del*] reading slowly over the names.—once again, if
you can, forgive me & believe me

> My dear Henslow
> Yours most truly
> C. Darwin

[1] Already in 1854 Darwin wrote in his Journal (*Bull. B.M. (N.H.)*, Vol. 2,
No. 1, p. 13): 'Began sorting notes for Species theory.' The question in the above
letter is on a problem on which he was particularly anxious to get more information—namely whether species of larger genera have more variation and a wider
geographical range than species of smaller genera. He had already completed his
two *Sketches* for his species theory as far back as 1842 and 1844. As I have mentioned in the Introduction, no suspicion of the extent to which his ideas of evolutionary theory had developed can be seen in the letters to Henslow. However, in

LETTER 82

[*To: Professor Henslow*
No postmark]

Down Farnborough Kent
July 2nd 1855

My dear Henslow

Very many thanks for all you have done, & so very kindly
promise to do for me.—

Will you make a present to each of the little girls (if not too big &
grandiose) of 6ᵈ. (for which I send stamps), who are going to
collect seeds for me.

viz Lychnis white

     ,,   red & flesh-colour (if such occur)

I shᵈ. greatly prefer Suffolk seeds to those which I could collect
myself, as a first little change.—

    Myosotis sylvatica

    Geum rivale   } Not quite ripe,

    Epilobium tetrag.   so as not to shed on Journey

& yet ripe enough (at least Epilobium) the [*that*] I may count
maximum, for which maximum, they ought to be fine [large
added] heads, about a dozen of each.—

Will you be so kind as to look at them [before sent *added*] just to
see positively that they are correct, for remember how ignorant
botanically I am—

Do you see Gardener's Chronicle, & did you notice some little
experiments of mine on salting seeds: Celery & Onion seed have
come up after 85 days immersion in the salt water, which seems
to me surprising, & I think throws some light on the wide
dispersion of certain plants.—Now it has occurred to me that it

---

the above letter we can get an exact date when he was dealing with the variation and
range of large and small genera. In 1855 he still meant to devote a whole chapter
to the subject in the larger work he then had in mind. After Wallace's simultaneous and independent statement of the theory of Natural Selection in 1858, which
forced on Darwin the need to complete in abridged form his *On the Origin of
Species* in 1859, the subject of variation and range of larger and smaller genera
is dealt with in Chap. II.

    See also Letters 82, 83 and 86 and Appendix 2.

would be an interesting way of testing the probability of sea-transportal of seeds, to make a list of all the Europaean plants found in the Azores,—a very [central *del*] oceanic archipelago,—collect the seeds & try if they would stand a pretty long immersion.—Do you think the most able of your little girls would like to collect for me a packet of seeds of such [azorean *added*] plants as grow near Hitcham, I paying, say 3ᵈ for each packet: it would put a few shillings into their pockets & would be an ENORMOUS advantage to me, for I grudge the time to collect the seeds, more especially, *as I have to learn the plants*!! The experiment seems to me worth trying; what do you think? shᵈ you object offering [for me *added*] this reward or payment to your little girls? you wᵈ have to select the most conscientious ones, that I might not get wrong seeds. I could return you your list marked, though I fear I shall have some little difficulty in knowing your [species *del*, English names *added*]. *No, no,* [I had forgotten your numbers *added*],—it will not [be difficult *added*] for I can order "Hooker & Arnotts'[1] Flora". Please tell me what edition, I have "Hooker's Botany" 4th Edition [but that is not in natural system *added*].—I have just been comparing the lists & I suspect you would not have very many of [the *added*] Azorean plants. You have, however,

Ranunculus repens
       „   parviflorus?
Papaver rhoeas?
      „   dubium?
Chelidonium majus?
Fumaria officinalis?
      „   [capreolata? *del*]

All these are Azorian plants.

---

[1] George Arnott Walker Arnott (1799–1868). Gave up law for botany; a close friend of Sir W. Hooker, with whom he collaborated in describing the plants of Beechey's voyage. In 1850 they issued the sixth edition of the *British Flora.* Walker Arnott became Professor of Botany at Glasgow in 1845 until his death in 1868. Sir William Hooker was elected to the Chair as its first occupant in 1820.

With respect to cultivating plants, I mean to begin on very few, for I may find it too troublesome: I have already had for some months primroses & cowslips, strongly manured with guano—& with flowers picked off, & one cowslip made to grow in shade, & next spring I shall collect seed.—I think you have quite misunderstood me in regard to my object in getting you to mark [in accompanying list *added*] with (X) [ALL *added*] the *"close species"* i.e. such as you do NOT *think* to [be *added*] varieties, but which nevertheless are *very closely* allied;—it has nothing whatever to do with their cultivation, but I cannot tell you [*the*] object, as it might unconsciously influence you in marking them. Will you draw your pencil right through all the names of those (few) species, of which you may know nothing. Afterwards when done I will tell you my object,—not that it is worth telling though I *myself* am very curious on [*the*] subject.—I know & can perceive that the definition of "close species" is *very vague*, & therefore I should not care for the list marked being marked by anyone except by such as yourself.—

Forgive this long letter, I thank you heartily for all your assistance.

> My dear old Master
> Yours affectionately
> C. Darwin

Perhaps 3^d would be hardly enough; & if the number [of kinds *added*] does not turn out very great it shall be 6^d per packet.

LETTER 83

[*To: Professor Henslow*
No postmark]

Down July 7th 1855

My dear Henslow

I write to thank you heartily for the seeds etc etc & all you have done. I do not think I have yet made it quite clear what I want marked in the Catalogue: (but I am really ashamed to be so troublesome) it is not so much what you *"think may turn out varieties"* (to quote your own words) but what you *think* are [really *added*] species, but [yet *added*] are very closely allied to some other species: I well know how vague this is, & perhaps you will find it impossible to do; but certainly, judging from all I have seen in animals, one pretty often meets a pair or more real (as far as one can judge) species, which yet are far more closely allied together than the average.

Of course there is always the possibility & even sometimes probability of these close species turning out varieties.—

Ever most truly yours
C. Darwin

Perhaps you might (if you can do the job) mark the closely allied species in connection, thus in an imaginary genus

```
Quercus pedunculata X
         rubra       |
         alba        |
         candida     |
         sessiliflora X
         alta        |
         humilis     X
```

I sh^d. understand by this that you thought Q. pedunculata sessiliflora & humilis VERY CLOSELY ALLIED species, but yet REAL species. I repeat perhaps that it will be impossible.—

LETTER 84

[*To: Professor Henslow*
No postmark]

Down Farnborough Kent
July 11th 1855

My dear Henslow
As I see Babington makes some differences between Lychnis diurna & vespertina; & as he says that the red species is sometimes white, & white sometimes red, it strikes me as quite necessary

that a *good* specimen, of the same plant [from which the seeds were got *added*] or from same group of plants sh^d be dried as a standard of comparison, sh^d I succeed in making the seedlings from your seed sport & vary.—Do you not think that this will be quite necessary?—otherwise it will be asserted that it was a *red var.* of L. vespertina. I have planted part of the seed in good sunny ground, & as soon as I can get young plants, I will begin to manure & torture [them *added*] in every way, which I can think of.—

I have, also, sown Myosotis in two situations; but I care most about the Lychnis, as Gærtner has laboriously experimented on its powers of crossing.

Ever your's most truly
C. Darwin

Do you think you could by any correspondent get me some seed of the wild Dianthus caryophyllus; I want some to try some experiments in hybridising. & I sh^d likewise like to see whether I could break the plant & get pretty varieties.—

LETTER 85

[*To: Professor Henslow*
No postmark]

Down Farnborough Kent
July 14th 1855

My dear Henslow.

With mistakes & alterations, the Hitcham list is so blotched, that I have copied out the 22 plants, which grow at Hitcham & are found at Azores; & are according to a list of 77 received yesterday, from Mr. H. C. Watson,[1] the least likely to have been imported with agricultural seeds.—If you will employ your little girls to collect these, I sh^d be greatly obliged, and pay them LIBERALLY

---

[1] Hewett Cottrell Watson, 1804–81, botanist and phrenologist, author of *Cybele Britannica* (1847–59), and founder of the study of distribution of the British Flora. Visited the Azores in 1842, and wrote on the plants in the *London Journal of Botany*, 1843–4.

for me. I sh^d require, when such could be procured, a packet with
100 or 200 seeds of each kind, or even rather more of the easily
procured kinds; of course less would do. But I have to try them
without salting, & at successive periods after immersion.—I
think I sh^d prefer waiting till you have a good many [of the 22
added] kinds together. I hope that you think the experiment
sufficiently curious to repay you in some slight degree for part of
[*the*] trouble you have so kindly taken. I hope that the little girls,
with payment in view, will enjoy the job.—

Most truly yours
C. Darwin

[*list of seed required*]
Water-cress—nasturtium officinale
Milkwort
[*Strawberry del*] Fragaria vesca
[*Silver weed del*] Cinque-foil, creeping Potentilla reptans
Cinquefoil strawberry-leaved P. tormentilla
[*Willow del*]—herb—small-flowered. Epilob. parviflorum.
Water-star-wort   Callitriche
Ivy   Hedera   helix
Marsh-wort procumbant   Helosciadium nodiflorum
Bedstraw, white water   Galium palustre
Centaury common   Erythræa centauria[1]
Hooded-Bindweed, great. Convolvulus sepium
Primrose   Primula veris
Figwort water   Scrophularia aquatica
Speedwell thyme-leaved. Veronica serpyllifolia
    „   water   „   anagallis
    „   common   „   officinalis
Thrincia hairy—   Thrincia hirta
Spurge-laurel, common   Daphne laureola
Club Rush, lake   Scirpus lacustris
Carex—   any 2 species

22 kinds

[1] 'Centauria' is a *lapsus calami* for *Centaurium*.—N. Y. S.

N

LETTER 86

[*To: Professor Henslow*
No postmark]

Down Farnborough Kent
July 21st [*1855*]

My dear Henslow

I really can hardly enumerate how many things I have to thank you for.—There is all that you are doing for me in the seed line, [including the wild Carnations *added*], the copies of the Hitcham List,—your Programme & your note telling me how well your Fete seems to have turned out. The Horners have been staying here, & Mr Horner tells me he was once with one of your Excursions, & he was full of admiration at all the doings at Hitcham,— as indeed everyone must be.—Your Botanical little girls are simply *marvellous*; I am so glad to hear that you intend writing some little Book to show how to teach [Botany *added*]: I find with my own children I hardly know how to begin.

I thank you much for attempting to mark the list of dubious species: I was afraid it was a very difficult task, from, as you say, the want of all definition of what a species is.—I think however you were marking exactly what I wanted to know. My wish was derived as follows: I have ascertained, that APPARENTLY [(I will not take up time by showing how) *added*] there is more variation, a wider geographical range, & probably more individuals, in the species of *large* genera than in the species of *small* genera. These general facts seem to me very curious, & I wanted to ascertain one point more; viz whether the closely allied & dubious forms, which are generally considered as species, also belonged [on average *added*] to large genera.—I shd like sometime to know where you have recorded your opinion that a change in the character of one organ induces other changes: for curiously I have this summer been planting *many* varieties (46 Peas) chiefly for the sake of observing this very point.—

Will you be so kind as to add *specially* to your list of desired seeds, the *white* Lychnis: for I have in vain endeavoured here to find the Plant.—Babington, I see, asserts that L. diurna & vespertina, differ (besides in colour) in form of capsule & in the teeth of the calyx. Gærtner further asserts that there is some difference in the period of their sleep, i.e. I suppose, closing their flowers: With all this, & as a guide to me to look out for the variable points, I sh^d like, if you have any opportunity, to have the red & white Lychnis dried for me by your little girls.—

I end this long note, by saying that I had intended coming to London before very long, & will come on 7th or 8th of August. But when it comes nearer the time, I will write & ask how I can have best chance of meeting you.

Ever your's most truly
C. Darwin

LETTER 87

[*To: Professor Henslow*
No postmark]

Down 23^d July 1855

My dear Henslow

It has just occurred to me that possibly you might be able to dine with me at my Brothers "57 Queen Anne St. Cavendish Sq^e" on either 7th or 8th of August, at 7 oclock *or any other hour.*—You can answer me whenever you like, & can see your way. I will try & get Hooker to come & dine there also. I sh^d like to know a few days before to let my Brothers Cook know,—If you can do say yes, it is a capital central situation.—

Ever your's
C. Darwin

LETTER 88

[*To Professor Henslow
No postmark*]

Down Farnborough *Kent*

N.B. Both your last letters have gone wrong from *Kent* having been omitted.—

July 28ᵗʰ—1855

My dear Henslow

I am delighted that you will come to dinner (7 oclock) to 57 Queen Anne St. on the 7ᵗʰ.—My Brother, who is staying here at present, tells me to suggest to you to sleep there, as there is a bed perfectly at your service: do if you can, for it will save you moving about & I shall see you at Breakfast.—

I have asked Hooker to dine with us.—

Very many thanks about Lychnis seed etc etc etc.—

Will you add one more thing to your list (& then I promise that I have done for a good long time) viz the entire umbel with RIPISH seed of the wild celery: I want to ascertain whether wild [(or half wild) *added*] or tame plants [of same species *added*] produce most seed.—

What wonderful, really wonderful little girls yours are in the Botanical line.—You ought to try (or I would) whether your curious Rose would yield any plants true by seed, if seed it produces.—

Ever most truly yours
C. Darwin

LETTER 89

[*To: Professor Henslow*
No postmark]

Down 23rd [*Aug/Sept 1855?*]

My dear Henslow

The enclosed Umbellifer has made me very unhappy: I *cannot* make it out: will you name it for me? I hate the whole Family. It grew [3–4 ft high *added*] in rather moist thicket. To save trouble I send envelope all ready directed.—On account of two statements made by naturalists, viz (one) that the most "typical form of a species is that which produces most seed," I am very anxious to compare number of seed of wild & cultivated plants (I can easily see how false the above aphorism is [but I want precise facts *added*]) & I most curiously forget it w^d. not suffice to count seeds of one umbel of Wild Celery so will you get one of your little girls to get very finest $\frac{1}{2}$ wild Celery near you, & either count (& pay well for me) all the seeds, or count umbels, & count seeds in an average umbel.—I can manage Carrot & Parsnip myself, & have wild & tame plants, marked. I have got Wild Cabbage & asparagus, also, in hand.—[our wild Parsnips are poor, so perhaps it w^d be good to let some little girl count *added*] There has been another more wonderful statement made than even the above,—viz that rich cultivation (not merely of the individual but of the race, *lessens* the fertility of all organic beings, by which assumption several [authors *added*] (as I daresay you may have noticed) have attempted to upset Malthus'[1] most logical writing —I mention all this just to show that my odd wishes are not *absolutely* idle. Most truly your's

C. Darwin

P.S. If you think fit you can entirely leave out such genera, as Rubus, Salix etc, in which I suppose hardly anyone knows what a

---

[1] Already in 1838 Darwin had read T. R. Malthus' *Essay on the Principle of Population*, 1798, and had found confirmation for his already conceived ideas, on Natural Selection. See *Autobiography*, p. 120, and *Bull. B.M.* (*N.H.*), Vol. 2, No. 4.

species is. By species I mean the ordinary rather vague accepta-
tion of the term. If you pass over any genus entirely, just score
out the generic name.

LETTER 90

[*To: Professor Henslow*
No postmark]

Down Bromley Kent
Oct. 12th [*1855?*]

My dear Henslow
I write one line to thank you for your note & Programme. I was,
also, interested by the brief account in the Gardeners' Chronicle.[1]
You little know how difficult, not to say impossible & how
awful it would be to many, & to myself for one, to lecture or
lecturette to a crowd of people. I would sooner pay 50£ for a good
lecturer to come here; but in the same proportions as I shd dread
such an undertaking, so do I honour you for all you do: how I
should like to see you at one of your Exhibitions! Before many
months are over I shall have to go over all my cirripedial collections & then I will not forget the Whale & Turtle parasites, if,
as I believe, I have any to spare. I have lately been reading in
M.S. an admirable essay by Hooker on variation,—geographical
range—& other such high & curious points etc. & it strikes [*me*]
as a first rate production, worthy of a son-in-law of yours.[2]
Ever my dear Henslow
Most truly yours
C. Darwin

[1] Henslow wrote frequently in the *Gardeners' Chronicle* from 1842 onwards,
covering a wide range of subjects, including accounts of his educational plans at
Hitcham and in museums.

[2] This must have been the *Introductory Essay to the Flora Indica*, about which
Hooker wrote in July 1855 to G. Bentham, who was in Paris for the Great Exhibition. Hooker was taking stock of the new ideas gained from his world's eye
view of botanical species and genera, and was in revolt against the orthodoxy of
the static view of species. He wrote: 'The Flora Indica Introd. Essay is going
ahead. Henfrey [Professor of Botany, King's College, London, 1853] is shot and
proposes altering his whole system of Botanical instruction at King's College;

LETTER 91

[*To: Professor Henslow*
No postmark]

Down Bromley Kent
Oct 29th [*1855*]

My dear Henslow

I received some time since the capital collection of Pois sans
Parchement & the Beet for which very many thanks, & still more
for your having got them so cheaply! I have seen Hooker since
his return & he told me a little about your goings on at Paris,[1]
which must have answered very well. I wish I had steam &
strength enough to go.

Whenever quite convenient will you send me off the seeds
which your little girls have collected for me, addressed as follows

C. Darwin Esq
Down
care of G. Snow
Nag's Head
Borough.

and then I must send a P. order as a present to the little collectors.
The plants from the Lychnis seed & Myosotis have come up

---

my chères confrères the geologists shrug their shoulders and do not half like it
. . . I have frightened them out of their wits, and some of them thank me for the
presentation copy with a frigidity that delights me. Hitherto Botany has been dull
work to me, little pay; no quarrels; an utter disbelief in the stability of my own
genera and species . . .' In the *Essay on the Tasmanian Flora*, published 1859, and
before the publication of *O* he expressed his views by using the Darwin–Wallace
theory of descent with modification as a working hypothesis, thus approaching his whole-hearted support for Darwin's views so soon to follow. See *Life and
Letters of Sir Joseph Hooker*, Vol. I, p. 374.
   [1] The Great Exhibition in Paris in 1855, rivalling the London exhibition of
1851. Henslow contributed a 'beautiful set of Carpological Illustrations, which
excited the enthusiasm of the Paris botanists, and of which a duplicate set is now
in the South Kensington Museum'. (Jenyn's *Memoir*, p. 159.) J. D. Hooker joined
Henslow in Paris in September, on his return from Germany, Austria and Italy.
Earlier, in a letter to G. Bentham, July, 1855, Hooker wrote: 'I did half promise to
go [to Paris] with Henslow, but he is disgusted with his wax models having
collapsed.' *Life of Hooker*, Vol. I, p. 434.

splendidly; & next spring their torments shall commence. Ever my dear Henslow, Your most truly

C. Darwin

My wife & self went to Glasgow[1] & we were disappointed in not meeting you, which we had calculated on. It was a good, but not very brilliant Meeting.—

LETTER 92

[*To: Professor Henslow*
No postmark]

Down Bromley Kent
Nov. 10th [*1855*]

My dear Henslow

I am *very much* obliged for the seeds, especially for the experimental seeds. I send a P. order for 10ˢ for a douceur for your good little Botanists, & I am sure the girl who counted the Parsnip seeds deserves a perfect dowry.—

It so happens, & not from caprice, that I care less for the seeds for salting, because I [before *del*, formerly *added*], from often having met accounts of floating plants off the mouths of estuaries I assumed that half-dried plants with their fruit or pods would certainly float for several weeks, but having tried some 30 or 40 plants I have found only a single one which floated after a month's immersion, & most sink after one week. So that I am almost foiled about sea-transportal. I may mention, the Capsicum seed germinated excellently after 137 days [immersion in salt-water *added*] & Celery pretty well after the same period.—I shall, however, finish my work & try those seeds which you have sent, & those which are not yet quite dry; [but pray take no more trouble on subject *added*].—

I have written & sent off a very gracious note to Mˢʳ Vilmorin. The seed of "Lychnis dioica in a field of Lucerne, Hitcham", I presume was the WHITE-flowered kind; I shall understand it to be

[1] British Association Meeting, under Presidency of Duke of Argyll, F.R.S.

so if I do *not hear to contrary*. Also as you were so kind as to superintend the counting of the Parsnip seed, I presume that of course the two seeds to each flower was calculated by the little girl.—

Do you remember saying that you thought that you could obtain for me information regarding Hollyocks. I am very curious on this subject & it is a curiosity of several years standing. I have myself made some experiments, & have got some apparently good crossed seeds & have castrated some [other *added*] plants & let the insects do their work, but I sh^d be particularly glad to hear what the great growers think; if you would, therefore, when at leisure (but this I fancy never comes, but when less busy than usual) send the enclosed queries (& there is no hurry) I sh^d be much obliged. —You will see I have headed the [letter *del*, queries *added*] with a note to you, the object of which is to show Mrss. Chator that I am intimate with you & therefore a respectable person. Very hearty thanks for all the trouble you take for me.

My dear Henslow
Most truly yours
C. Darwin

LETTER 93

[*To: Professor Henslow*
No postmark]

Down Bromley Kent
18th Dec 1855

My dear Henslow
I write one line to say that I have received the seeds safely & to thank you very much for them.—

What a weeks work you have cut out for yourself! I shall be in London on Friday, but I see no chance of our meeting.—

Yours most truly
C. Darwin

LETTER 94

[*To: Professor Henslow*
No postmark]

> Down Bromley Kent
> Dec. 26th 1855

My dear Henslow,
Will you look over the little book on Clubs sent with this.—It amused me, but it has frightened me about our Club, of which I am Treasurer & in fact Guardian. By the way our Club is in some degree your offspring.—What I want to hear is whether you think enrolled Clubs can be in such a dangerous state as he makes all Clubs to be in. I have thought of sending full statement to some Actuary for his opinion: can you give me any advice.—Secondly, I have thought to advise our Club *not* to grant pensions for it has, as yet, not granted one. Thirdly, do you think it w^d be possible to enact a rule that the Club should buy off any member who went to reside at distance; but I fear that members would object, & I presume an Actuary would have to calculate value in each case. What think you? Certainly a Club has very little check over a distant member.—Will you return little book which has been lent me by Mr. Innes.[1]

> Yours most truly
> C. Darwin

LETTER 95

[*To: Professor Henslow*
No postmark]

> Down Bromley Kent
> Jan 3rd [*1856*]

My dear Henslow
I have received your letter, the Report & pamphlet, for all of which very many thanks.—Your letter has been of *real* use to

[1] Vicar of Down since 1846; see Letter 73, p. 167, in which Benefit Clubs are discussed. Clearly, one of the purposes of the Down Club was to encourage saving.

me, in deciding what to do, which will be, in consequence, very little.

What trouble Government does give about Clubs.—I have been two whole days in drawing up the annual & Quinquennial Returns! Farewell with many thanks.—Pray remember to let me have the case of the [Canada *added*] Geese with the seed in crop, if ever you sh^d meet with it; as the *means* of distribution is, at present, a great hobby with me.—

Farewell
C. Darwin

Your servants relation failed, I presume, in getting the wild Carnation seed from Rochester.—

LETTER 96

[To: Professor Henslow
No postmark]

Down Bromley Kent
Jan. 22nd [*1856*]

My dear Henslow

I write merely to thank you for your note, though my former one did not require an answer.

I have entirely forgotten (& it is stupid of me) that you had told me about the wild carnation seed.—

Mr Tollet[1] (W. Clive's father in law) *is* dead.—Have you seen A. de Candolle's Geographie Botanique:[2] it strikes me as a quite wonderful & admirable work.—

I saw in the Times the death of your Mother, but at so venerable an age that life can hardly be to any worth much further

---

[1] Possibly Mr Tollet of Betley Hall near Maer, a liberal squire and experimenter in agriculture, whose daughters were great friends of the Wedgwoods.

[2] Alphonse de Candolle, 1806-93, son of the botanist Augustin Pyrame de Candolle, published his important *Géographie Botanique*, 2 vols., in 1855.

prolongation. In one sense I never knew what this greatest of losses is, for I lost my mother in very early childhood.—

My dear Henslow
Yours most truly
Charles Darwin

P.S.
I have been sowing some of the seeds from Hitcham this morning.

LETTER 97

[*To: Professor Henslow*
No postmark]

Down Bromley Kent
June 16th [*1856?*]

My dear Henslow
You may remember sending me seed of "Myosotis repens or cæspitosa, Stowmarket". The next time you go that way, would you be so kind as to gather me a tuft in flower & send it in letter that I may see what the aboriginal is like.—I send one of my cultivated spec^s. (1st generation) that you may see it, not that I suppose it is anyways remarkable.—
Secondly, can you give me the address of shop in London, where, years ago, I got on your recommendation [nice *added*] square strong paste-board Boxes, about 15 inches square: I cannot myself remember in the least where it was.—*Thirdly*. when will you publish some little Book to show how to teach Botany on Nat. System to children: How I wish you would: my children are always asking me, & I have no idea how to begin. If you can't or won't publish pray tell me what Book I had better get: Lindley's School Bot. is out of Print, which Hooker recommended to me; —not that, I suppose, that would have done to teach children by. —Forgive my 3 questions, & answer them when at leisure, or rather when least busy.

My dear Henslow
Yours most truly
C. Darwin

Your Lychnis-plants are flourishing & I am dosing them & others, with Guano water, salt-petre & common salt, & intend thus to make the most wonderful transformation—that is, if the plants have any gratitude, for they evidently much like the doctoring.—

[*INCOMPLETE*] LETTER 98

[*1856*]

You can tear off to first page & send it to Fisher & you will have no more trouble on subject.—

I was very glad to have your letter & hear a little news of you.— Your success with your village girls strikes me as nothing less than marvellous.

I am delighted to hear how well your son is going on, & that the by me truly honoured name of Henslow will have a Botanical successor.[1]—We are all pretty well, & my Boys are now d.6— Is it not awful? I am working away steadily & very hard at my work on Variation & I find the whole subject deeply interesting, but horribly perplexed.—

My dear Henslow
Your affectionate old Pupil
C. Darwin

[1] In Jan. 1856, J. D. Hooker wrote to J. S. Henslow on George Henslow's career: 'Keep him to botany if you can, but not to the exclusion of other pursuits, drawing etc. I am well sure that there will be openings and good ones for accomplished Botanists ere long....' L. Huxley's *Life and Letters of J. D. Hooker*, Vol. I, p. 374.

George took orders and became Honorary Professor to the Royal Horticultural Society. He was a prolific writer and speaker on botanical subjects; the separates from current publications between 1871–1915 occupy eleven bound volumes in the Linnean Library, indexed in his own hand, and interleaved with interesting MS letters from his correspondents. George Henslow believed in the inheritance of acquired characters in plants, and combated the newly recognised work of August Weismann. He wrote a review of Weismann's *Theory of Heredity applied to Plants in Natural Science*, Vol. I, No. 3, 1892. The following letter from Herbert Spencer is bound up in MS. with the review. 'Thank you for

LETTER 99

[*To: Professor Henslow*
No postmark]

Down Farnborough Kent[1]
Aug. 6th 1856

My dear Henslow

I received your letter dated 2nd only yesterday: I shall not come to Cheltenham, though your presence & L. Jenyns paper would be a great temptation.

I am particularly pleased to hear about the Centaurea, the seed, which you gave me did not germinate. Your Ægilops has come up & has ripened seed: I forced it so as not to flower at same time with wheat: it has not varied: you formerly called it Ae. Ovata now Ae. Squarrosa.—

The Myosotis was [slightly forced planted out *del*] sown in open ground, both in sunny & shady places; in former place, whence the specimens sent to you came, it was watered weekly with Guano water. Nearly all the flowers are brightish blue, & only a very few on dwarf branches are pink. The specimens in the more shady place have the lobes of corolla slightly emarginate. The tube of corolla, in comparison with the calyx seems to be longer in the blue than in the smaller pinkish flowers.

With respect to seeds; I shd be extremely glad of any water plants; especially of Callitriche verna, Limosella aquatica and Montana[2] fontana, (if such you have).—I want, also, to try whether the right

---

your two papers. I am glad to have so efficient a co-combatant, believing as I do that the erroneous doctrines of Weismann are doing a great deal of mischief. . . . My own feeling with regard to Weismann's doctrines is that the wide acceptance of them is nothing less than a disgrace to the biological world. . . .'

George Henslow's views upholding the inheritance of acquired characters carried little weight. He was antagonistic towards Natural Selection, perhaps not realising Darwin's own uncertainties. But he was the first to recognise Darwin as England's first ecologist.

[1] In spite of this address—which should have been altered to Bromley in 1855— I have placed this letter here on account of the Cheltenham British Association Meeting, which took place in 1856 under the Presidency of Professor Charles Daubeny, F.R.S.

[2] 'Montana' is a slip for *Montia* (*Montia fontana*).—N. Y. S.

pods on heads of seed would float in sea-water; if you could help me by sending a few specimens in Box by Post. I have just been correcting my paper on salting seeds for Linnean Journal.[1]

My dear Henslow

Yours most truly

Ch. Darwin

The seed of Rosa tomentosa did not come up.—

[UNPLACED NOTE]

[*1856?*]

I think you once wrote on vibrios[2] in wheat; I found the other day an Agrostis with every germen, (at least I opened a full dozen), with 1 or 2, or 3 little worms in them, & no [another *del*] stamens or stigmas.—

I am working at all varieties & have now got 46 kinds of Peas all growing together.

LETTER 100

[*To: Professor Henslow
No postmark*]

Down Bromley Kent

Aug. 10th [*1857?*]

My dear Henslow

I am delighted at your letter just received.

For fear of a mistake, I write to say the Train leaves London Bridge (N. Kent Division) at 5.20'—(not *5.30'*) & remember how

---

[1] 'On the action of sea-water on the Germination of Seeds', *Linn. Soc. Journ.*, Vol. I, 1857 (Botany), pp. 130–40.

[2] Professor Henslow worked for many years at the damage to crops through the action of insects and fungi, his first 'Report on the Diseases in Wheat' being published in *Journ. Roy. Ag. Soc.*, 1841, Vol. II, part I. See Jenyns' *Memoir* of Henslow, p. 190 et seq. I find *Vibrio tritica* given as the name of the galls of wheat-eelworm in Ormerod's *Manual of Injurious Insects*, 1890, also called 'Ear-cockles', 'Purples', and 'False Ergot'.

crowded near London Bridge is.—Our last visitors missed the
Train.—We will send you back at any time on Friday you like.

Ever yours
C. Darwin

LETTER 101

[*To: Professor Henslow
No postmark*]

Down Bromley Kent
Oct. 14th [*1857?*]

My dear Henslow

It is a great shame to trouble you about such trifles; but your
Myosotis is beginning to sport under my treatment; & I want to
know whether it is not an odd thing some of the calyces, (as the
one separate one) having 6 nuts.—Some twigs produce green
flowers, with the nuts oddly elongated; of which I send a little
twig, I do not send more, as I want to save the monstrous seeds.—
The shortest scrap in answer anytime w^d much oblige me.

Most truly yours
C. Darwin

LETTER 102

[*To: Professor Henslow
No postmark*]

Down Bromley Kent
Oct. 18th 1857

My dear Henslow

I write to thank you for your note & to say that I sh^d be VERY
glad to have your Photograph.—You c^d leave it for me at Royal
Soc. or Linn. Soc. or Athenaeum Club, wherever most convenient to you.—
The plant with green flowers was this year's seedling: but
apparently [on *del*] only certain twigs on same plant were thus
characterised. I had fancied that the 6 seeds was older part; but

after sending you the specimen, I found flower with 10 sepals and two pistils & 8 or 10 imperfect seeds—; & other flowers with only 3 seeds.—

I feel pretty sure I could make any flower in some degree monstrous in 4 or 5 generations.

I am very glad to hear of the grand success of the Hitcham Hort. Soc. it must be very pleasant to you.—

I notice the Death of your Aunt. If you keep your health God grant you may live as long.

Most truly yours
C. Darwin

LETTER 103

[*To: Professor Henslow*
No postmark]

Down Bromley Kent
Jan 25th 1858

My dear Henslow

I received the day before yesterday the appendix to the allotment Report & I am glad to see how eminently successful your men have been.—I have not written to you, as I thought it would only have troubled & I was very sure that you need not be told how sincerely & deeply I have sympathised with you,[1]—to whom I shall ever owe so much. Those old days when I used as an undergraduate to be so much at your house were certainly amongst the most happy & best days which I have ever spent. Never shall I forget to end of my life the uniform & very great kindness of poor dear Mrs. Henslow to me.—I hope you are all well & that your health is pretty good: I have heard not a very good account of your appearance.—I *beg* you not to think of answering this note. My dear friend & most kind old master

Believe me
Yours affectionately
Ch. Darwin

[1] On the death of his wife.

o

LETTER 104

[*To: Professor Henslow*
No postmark]

Norfolk House
Shanklin Is. of Wight
Aug. 4th 1858

My dear Henslow

Your letter of the 31st has been forwarded to me here & received only this morning. I grieve most sincerely to miss your visit, but we do not return home till the 13th or 14th & my wife, perhaps not till later: if the sea does my eldest girl[1] good. We were driven from home by Scarlet Fever, which caused the death of our poor dear little youngest child & was very bad in the village. We had other & bad illness in the House. As yet the sea has not done much for us.—I the more regret that we shall not see you at Down at the time proposed, (but I hope at some other time) as I sh^d be extremely glad (& grateful) to hear your objections to my species speculations.

The difficulties which I can see are many & grave. I am now writing a pretty full abstract of all my notions on this subject.—

My dear Henslow
Your old affectionate pupil
C. Darwin

P.S.

I want to beg a favour of you, which will cost you writing a note, viz can you advise us what I ought to allow my eldest son[2] who goes to X [*Christ's*] Coll. in October per annum to cover ALL his expenses whatever.—I can afford & sh^d wish to give him a liberal allowance, but not to encourage extravagance.

[1] Henrietta, born 1843, married R. B. Litchfield 1871.
[2] William Erasmus Darwin, 1839–1914. Became a banker in Southampton.

LETTER 105

[*To: Professor Henslow*
No postmark]

Down Bromley Kent
Sept. 25th [*1858?*]

My dear Henslow
I have this minute [*been*] writing to my son at Rugby to tell him of your magnificent present. The Coffer [?] will especially delight him; & I write now to give you our hearty thanks. I hope Hooker will come here this autumn & then he will bring the specimens; & if he does not come I must run over to Kew for a day. Please remember sometime when at Ipswich to enquire whether water-fowl have ever been seen on the great tank of Mr. Ransome's.

Ever my dear Henslow
Your's most truly
C. Darwin

LETTER 106

[*To: Professor Henslow*
No postmark]

Down Bromley Kent
Nov 9th 1858

My dear Henslow
We shall be truly delighted to see you here on the 25th.—If you will send me one line to say by what hour you will be at Croydon, in all probability I shall be able to send to meet you with my phaeton.—If you go to London, from Sir B. then come to *Beckenham* either by [C. Palace *del*] the Pimlico or London Bridge line.—I fear I have not strength to meet you at C. Palace.—

My dear Henslow
Yours most truly
C. Darwin

LETTER 107

[*To: Professor Henslow*

Down, November 11th, 1859

My dear Henslow,

I have told Murray to send a copy of my book on Species to you, my dear old master in Natural History; I fear, however, that you will not approve of your pupil in this case. The book in its present state does not show the amount of labour which I have bestowed on the subject.

If you have time to read it carefully, and would take the trouble to point out what part seems weakest to you and what best, it would be a most material aid to me in writing my bigger book, which I hope to commence in a few months. You know also how highly I value your judgment. But I am not so unreasonable as to wish or expect you to write detailed or lengthy criticism but merely a few general remarks, pointing out the weakest parts.

If you are *in even so slight a degree* staggered (which I hardly expect) on the immutability of species, then I am convinced with further reflection you will become more and more staggered, for this has been the process through which my mind has gone. My dear Henslow,

Yours affectionately and gratefully,
C. Darwin

LETTER 108

[*To: Professor Henslow*
No postmark]

Down. Feb 3rd 1860

My dear Henslow
Many thanks for L. Jenyns very sensible letter.—We shall be truly delighted to see you whenever you can come, after the 11th or any other time.—In Haste

Most truly yours
C. Darwin

LETTER 109

[*To: Professor Henslow*
No postmark]

Down Bromley Kent
Feb 9th 1860

My dear Henslow

We shall be *delighted* to see you on 14th. Trains leave London Bridge [N. Kent station *added*] for Bromley (NOT Shortland Station) at 1°.30'. 3.30, 4.40, 5.40. If you can tell me by what train you will come, I will endeavour to send carriage to meet you: if it sh^d not be there, you must take Fly at Station—6 miles here.—

In haste
Yours affect
C. Darwin

LETTER 110

[*To: Professor Henslow*
No postmark]

Down Bromley Kent
Ap. 2nd 1860

My dear Henslow

I write one line to remind you to be so kind as to give me a sketch & account of the wasp's comb in transitional state from horizontal to vertical, & the county whence procured. etc. etc.—[1]

As I am in the way of reminding, I will remind about Anacharis —viz how far it has travelled up the Cherry Hinton-Brook—how long the journey has consumed, the means etc.—I have since you were here found statement [by Babington *added*] that this plant is now not so common as it was at first introduction. I sh^d very much like to have this confirmed, & what creatures destroy it.—

---

[1] The cell-making instinct of the hive-bee is dealt with in *O*, p. 224 et seq. first edition; & p. 220, 1872 ed. This was a subject that fascinated Darwin, involving the inheritance of immensely complex instincts, and he was always collecting fresh evidence on such themes.

Lastly what plants in any particular spot or pond it has nearly or quite exterminated by taking their places? Here is a goodly list of queries!

Many thanks for your Sermon & for copies of the Examination Papers received some time since. Sedgwick's was not very fair towards the students; but Murray, the Publisher, thought it splendid for selling copies to the unfortunate Students.[1]

My dear Henslow
Yours very truly
C. Darwin

LETTER III

[*C.U.L. from a copy*]
[*To: Charles Darwin*
From: Prof. J. S. Henslow]

7 Downing Terrace, Cambridge
5 May, 1860

My dear Darwin

I read your wishes to my Class and yesterday after Lecture a few of us walked to Cherry Hinton. I found the Elodea had made great progress since I saw it a year or two ago. It is now quite up to the source of the stream and fills the ditches in Cherry Hinton itself. But I find this stream is not connected with the water-course that runs past the Botanic Garden (as I had supposed) but runs down to the paper mills beyond Barnwell. It seems therefore to have travelled up from the river itself which is full of it. So far as mere recollection guides me it seems to have greatly diminished the quantity of *Ranunculus aquatilis var. fluitans* which used to abound in the stream at the part we visited. It decidedly preponderates over every other aquatic, but I found it associated with *Potamogeton densus* (in small quantity) and *Ranunculus aquatilis*, and intermixed with plenty of *Lemna tri-*

---

[1] *On the Origin of Species* was published by John Murray in November 1859. Amongst the most bitter scientific opponents were Sedgwick and Owen.

sulca. Sedgwick is to illuminate us on Monday at the Philosophical Society in regard to your supposed errors! How can Owen be so savage with your views when his own are to a certain extent of the same character. If I understand him, he thinks the "Becoming" of species (I suppose he means the *producing* of species) a somewhat rapid and not a slow process—but he seems to think them *progressive* organised out of previously organized beings—{analogous (?) to minerals (simple and compound) out of some $\pm$ 60 Elements}.

I don't think it is at all *becoming* in one Naturalist to be bitter against another any more than for one sect to burn the members of another. Kind regards to Mrs. D. etc.

Yours affectionately
J. S. Henslow

LETTER 112

[*To: Professor Henslow*
No postmark]

Down Bromley Kent
May 8th [*1860*]

My dear Henslow

Very many thanks about the Elodea,—which case interests me much. I wrote to Mr Marshall at Ely & in due time he says he will send me whatever information he can procure.—Owen[1] is indeed very spiteful. He misrepresents & alters what I say very unfairly. But I think his conduct towards Hooker most ungenerous, viz to allude to his Essay, & not to notice the magnificent results on geographical distribution. The Londoners say he is mad with envy because my book has been talked about: what a strange man to be envious of a naturalist like myself immeasurably his inferior! From one conversation with him I really suspect he goes [at the bottom of his hidden soul *added*] as far as I do!—I wonder

---

[1] For Richard Owen, see footnote 2, Letter 44, p. 118, and footnote 2, Letter 116, p. 209.

whether Sedgwick noticed in the Edinburgh Review, about the "Sacerdotal reviler"—so the revilers are tearing each other to pieces.—I suppose Sedgwick will be very fierce against me at the Phil. Soc. [(on May 7) *added*].—Judging from his notice in the Spectator he will misrepresent me, but it will *certainly* be unintentionally done.—In a letter to me, & in the above notice, he talks much about my departing [about *del*] from the spirit of inductive philosophy.—I wish, if you ever talk on subject to him, you would ask him whether it was not allowable (& a great step) to invent the undulatory theory [of light *added*]—i e hypothetical undulations, in a hypothetical substance, the ether. And if this be so, why may I not invent hypothesis of natural selection (which from analogy of domestic productions, & from what we know of the struggle of existence & of the variability of organic beings, is, in some very slight degree, in itself probable) & try whether this hypothesis of natural selection does not explain (as I think it does) a large number of facts in geographical distribution—geological succession—classification—Morphology, embryology etc etc.— I sh^d really much like to know why such an hypothesis as the undulations of the ether may be invented, & why I may not invent (not that I did *invent* it, for I was led to it by studying domestic varieties) any hypothesis, such as natural selection. Pray forgive me & my pen for running away with me & scribbling on at such length.

My dear old Master
Your affec^t
C. Darwin

I can perfectly understand Sedgwick or anyone saying that nat. selection does not explain large classes of facts; but that is very different from saying that I depart from right principles of scientific investigation.—

LETTER 113

[*This letter from Prof. Henslow to J. D. Hooker, taken from 'Life and Letters of Sir J. D. Hooker' by L. Huxley, Vol. I, p. 512, shows Henslow's judgement on Darwin's views and is printed in part here with kind permission of Sir John Murray.*]

To: Sir Joseph Hooker
From: Professor J. S. Henslow

7 Downing Terrace, Cambridge
May 10, 1860

My dear Joseph,

I don't know whether you care to hear Phillips, who delivers the Rede Lecture in the Senate House next Tuesday at 2 p.m. It is understood that he means to attack the Darwinian hypothesis of Natural Selection.

Sedgwick's address last Monday was temperate enough for his usual mode of attack, but strong enough to cast a *slur* upon all who substitute hypotheses for strict inductions, and as he expressed himself in regard to some of C.D.'s suggestions as *revolting* to his own sense of right and wrong, and as Dr. Clark, who followed him, spoke so unnecessarily severely against Darwin's views, I got up, as Sedgwick had alluded to me, and stuck up for Darwin as well as I could, refusing to allow that he was guided by any but truthful motives, and declaring that he himself believed he was exalting and not debasing our views of a Creator, in attributing to him a power of imposing laws on the Organic World by which to do his work, as effectually as his laws imposed on the inorganic had done it in the Mineral Kingdom.

I believe I succeeded in diminishing, if not entirely removing, the chances of Darwin's being prejudged by many who take their cue in such cases according to the views of those they suppose may know something of the matter. Yesterday at my lectures I alluded to the subject, and showed how frequently Naturalists were at fault in regarding as *species*, forms which had (in some cases) been shown to be varieties, and how legitimately Darwin had deduced his *inferences* from positive experiment. Indeed I had on

Monday replied to a sneer (I don't mean from Sedgwick) at his pigeon results, by declaring that the case *necessitated* an appeal to such *domestic* experiments, and that this was the legitimate and best way of proceeding for the detection of those laws which we are endeavouring to discover.

I do not disguise my own opinion that Darwin has pressed his hypothesis too far, but at the same time I assert my belief that his Book is (as Owen described it to me) the 'Book of the Day'. I suspect the passages I marked in the *Edinburgh Review* for the illumination of Sedgwick have produced an impression upon him to a certain extent. When I had had my say, Sedgwick got up to explain, in a very few words, his good opinion of Darwin, but that he wished it to be understood that his chief attacks were directed against Powell's[1] late Essay from which he quoted passages as 'from an Oxford Divine' that would astound Cambridge men, as no doubt they do. He showed how greedily (if I may so speak) Powell has adopted all Darwin has suggested, and applied these suggestions (as if the whole were already proved) to his own views.

I think I have given you a fair, though very hasty, view of what happened and as I have just had a letter from Darwin, and really have not a minute to spare for a reply this morning, perhaps you will send this to him, as he may like to know, to some extent, what happened.

LETTER 114

[*To: Professor Henslow*
No postmark]

> Down Bromley Kent
> May 14th 1860

My dear Henslow

I have been greatly interested by your letter to Hooker; & I must thank you from my heart for so generously defending me as far

[1] The Rev. Baden Powell, 1796–1860, F.R.S., Savilian Professor of Geometry at Oxford. Author of *Essays on the spirit of the inductive philosophy, the unity of*

as you could against my powerful attackers.—Nothing which persons say hurts me for long, for I have entire conviction that I have not been influenced by bad feelings in the conclusions at which I have arrived. Nor have I published my conclusions without long deliberations & they were arrived at after far more study than the publick will ever know of or believe in.—I am certain to have erred in many points, but I do not believe so much as Sedgwick and Co. think. Is there any Abstract or Proceedings of the Cambridge Phil. Soc. published? If so & you could get me a copy I sh^d like to have one.

Believe me my dear Henslow I feel grateful to you on this occasion & for the multitude of kindnesses you have done me from my earliest days at Cambridge.—

Yours affectionately
C. Darwin

P.S. I think I remember your observing that the pistil in different flowers of cowslips & Primroses varies much in length. From observations which I have been making I have strong suspicion that they (& Auriculas) are dioicous [*dioecious*]; but I shall know this autumn for I have marked what I consider the male & female plants.[1] Why I mention this to you is that I have a vague remembrance of your stating that some other plants varied *greatly* in

---

worlds, *the philosophy of Creation*, 1855. See *Notes and Records of the Royal Society of London*, Vol. 14, No. 1, p. 51, 'Some unpublished letters of Charles Darwin', ed. Sir Gavin de Beer, F.R.S.

[1] From 1860, when the bulk of work on *O*, apart from new editions, was off his mind, Darwin threw himself into a series of books on botanical problems, always with an evolutionary background of variation and Natural Selection in view. This is the first mention of his interest in dimorphism—later to include trimorphism also: firstly published in two papers to the Linnean Society on Feb. 20, 1868, under the title:—'On the Character and Hybrid-like Nature of the Offspring from the Illegitimate Unions of Dimorphic and Trimorphic Plants'; and on Mar. 19, 1868, a second paper was read, entitled: 'On the Specific Difference between Primula Veris [etc.], P. Vulgaris [etc] and P. elatior—With Supplementary Remarks on naturally-produced Hybrids in the genus Verbascum'. The completed book, *The different Forms of Flowers on Plants of the Same Species*, was not published until 1877. He had to abandon his first idea that this dimorphism was a step towards a dioecious state.

length of pistil: if so I sh^d MUCH like to know what; that I might carefully observe them. Do not think of writing unless you can tell me of any such plants.—

LETTER 115

[*To: Professor Henslow*
No postmark]

Down Bromley Kent
May 17th [*1860*]

My dear Henslow
Many thanks for your note & information about my opposers.— I have sent for Literary Gazette.—For the chance of your caring I send the characters by which I can divide *all* Primroses & cowslips into what I suspect will turn out Male & Female Plants. These two forms exist in about equal numbers.—I have marked a set of both forms to see about seeding. The difference in state of pollen is very clear & invariable. I suspect it will turn out fine case for me: the first gradation in the formation of a dioicous plant.—The Holly forms a second step for here the Male plant has anthers but no pollen—The male cowslips have *abundant* pollen, but all grains small-sized.—It will be curious if I can show that so common a plant is dioicous or nearly so.
Auriculas are in same state as far as I have seen.—This is reason why I wanted to know whether you had observed long & short pistils in any other flowers.

Yours affect^y
C. Darwin

Cowslips & Primroses

Male Plants. Tube of corolla long, throat short—Stamens long— pollen [in water *added*] about $\frac{9}{60000}$ of inch in [(1$\frac{1}{2}$) $\frac{3}{2}$ $\times$ $\frac{1}{1000}$ *added*] diameter. Pistil short, stigma far beneath anthers,—surface of stigma smoother

Female plants:—Tube of corolla short, throat long.—Stamens short, pollen [in water *added*] about $\frac{6}{6000}$ of inch [1 . $\frac{1}{1000}$ *added*] in diameter:—Pistil long, stigma far above anthers, surface of stigma rougher.—

[♂ di : ♀ di :: 3 : 2 *added*]

LETTER 116

[*To: Professor Henslow*
No postmark]

at Miss Wedgwoods
Hartfield Tonbridge Wells
July 16ᵗʰ [*1860*]

My dear Henslow

I thought it wᵈ be better to write direct to Daubeny[1] & tell him there was nothing *direct* on subject in my Book.—I did not see much in his paper.—The frequency of "Sports" i.e. modified buds in plants goes direct against his views. There is no greater mystery in the whole world, as it seems to me, than the existence of sexes,—more especially since the discovery of Parthenogenesis.[2] The origination of sexes seems beyond all speculation.—

[1] Charles Giles Bridle Daubeny, F.R.S., 1795–1867. Elected firstly Professor of Chemistry at Oxford, 1822; then in 1834 became Professor of Botany, and 1840 Professor of Rural Economy. At the meeting of the British Association in Oxford in June, 1860, Dr Daubeny gave to the Zoological Section an address on 'The Final Causes of the Sexuality in Plants, with Particular Reference to Mr. Darwin's Work on the Origin of Species', to which he mainly gave his support. Owen and Huxley were both present, and Henslow was in the Chair. Antagonisms were revealed, but the famous clash of opinions came two days later, with Henslow again in the Chair, after an American Professor Draper's paper on the 'Intellectual Development of Europe, Considered with Reference to the Views of Mr. Darwin and Others.' A packed assembly came to hear the great men cut each other's throats, and Samuel Wilberforce's superficial ridicule and appeals to prejudice made him an easy prey to Huxley's eloquent and famous reply. See *LL*, II, p. 322.

[2] Richard Owen had collected the current knowledge of Parthenogenesis, as he construed it, in his Hunterian Lecture, 1849. T. H. Huxley took up the question in *Trans. Linn. Soc.*, Vol. XXIII, pp. 193 and 221, 'On the Reproduction of Aphis'. He examined with care the earlier work on the subject, some excellent, and made valuable experimental observations of his own. He then quoted eight sentences in

Nevertheless I quite agree with your remarks in answer to Daubeny.—

I am glad to hear M[rs?] Barnard's affair is safely over.—How successful your Fete seems to have been! In Haste

My dear old Master

Your affect.

C. Darwin

I did not hear of poor FitzRoy with the Bible at the Geographical Section—I think his mind is often on Verge of insanity.—

Owen's publication, statements repeated in Owen's second edition of his *Lectures on the Invertebrae.* Huxley commented: 'The paragraphs I have cited contain two kinds of propositions—assertions with regard to matters of fact, and deductions from those assertions. The former are, according to my observations, incorrect; and, as I conceive, the latter are unfounded.'

Darwin wrote to Huxley (*ML*, I, p. 103, probably in 1857): 'I am extremely glad you have taken up the Aphis question, but for Heaven's sake, do not come the Mild Hindoo (whatever he may be) over Owen; . . . I cannot but think that the same power is concerned in producing aphides without fertilisation, and producing, for instance, nails on the amputated stump of a man's fingers, or the new tail of a lizard . . . I am particularly glad that you are ruminating on the act of fertilisation; it has long seemed to me the most wonderful and curious of problems . . . Approaching the subject from the side which attracts me most, viz., inheritance, I have lately been inclined to speculate, very crudely and indistinctly, that propagation by true fertilisation will turn out to be a sort of mixture, and not true fusion, of two individuals, as each parent has its parents and ancestors. I can understand on no other view the way in which crossed forms go back to so large an extent to ancestral forms.' Darwin shows in this letter that flash of insight on the integrity of the unit character in inheritance that needed years of work by others to place on a firm basis. Yet in spite of this flash, Darwin's botanical experiments discussed in his letters to Henslow were often based on the belief in the inheritable response to treatment. Mendel in 1857 was already working at Brnō on the inheritance of unit characters, though unknown to Darwin; nor was his work fully recognised until after 1900. The conflicting concepts were to remain unresolved in Darwin's mind, and indeed are still a focal point of research.

The letter to Huxley also shows how different was the tone and content of Darwin's communications to his scientific friends in these later years from his correspondence with Henslow.

LETTER 117

[*To: Professor Henslow*
No postmark]

15 Marine Parade Eastbourne.
28th Sep. 1860

My dear Henslow

Just before coming here for our poor girl's health (I am glad to say that she has benefitted decidedly from sea-air) I received your little note, telling me that you were not quite satisfied on antiquity of the Celts. I fear that this truly dreadful weather will give me no chance of my weed-seeds.—My object in writing now is to beg for a bit of information; & I cannot think of any one else to apply to, otherwise I would not have troubled you.—

I have been making a great number of observations on the leaves of Drosera, & have come to some curious results about their power of discriminating nitrogenised compounds.—[1]

When the viscid hairs contract or become inflected; they pour out much fluid & the contents of the cells in the footstalks, instead of being a thin [pink *added*] homogenous fluid, becomes a broken mass of dark red, thick fluid. When the cells are in this condition, the particles circulate round the cell, *as if* driven by ciliae. I believe that this is not an uncommon circumstance: is it? But what has surprised me is that the globules & cylinders of the thick dark red fluid or substance keeps on an incessant *slow* contracting & expanding movement: they often coalesce & then separate again; they often send out buds, which rapidly increase at the expence of the larger parents mass; [in short endless slow changes in form *added*]. These slow incessant movements, which are quite independent of the circulation, resemble the movements of sarcode in the protozoa. Is any such phenomenon known? It may be quite

[1] In Darwin's Journal, *Bull. B.M.* (*N.H.*), Vol. 2, No. 1, p. 15, Darwin wrote: 'Aug. 11 [*1860*] Began Ch. III [*Animals and Plants under Domestication*]. During July at Hartfield [*home of Sara Wedgwood*] and afterwards at Eastbourne worked on Drosera.' This work culminated in *Insectivorous Plants* (John Murray, 1875), a subject on which very little work had been done. His main experimental work was carried out on the British species, *Drosera rotundifolia*, or Sundew.

common, as I am so ignorant of vegetable physiology.—It has surprised me much. Will you be so very kind, whenever you have a little leisure, to let me hear—I hope you have returned well & strong after your tour. What a wonderful start this of Hooker's.![1]

My dear Henslow
Yours affectionately
C. Darwin

P.S. Though I cannot conceive how it can be effected, I presume that the movements in the red matter must be due to slow absorption of water. Yet how this should make the globules coalesce, divide, coalesce again & bud out with new globules, it is hard to understand.

LETTER 118

[*To: Professor Henslow*
No postmark]

15 Marine Parade Eastbourne
Oct. 11 [*1860*]

My dear Henslow
Very many thanks for your pleasant letter just received from Down, with many things which interested me. I am particularly obliged for answer about contracting & expanding red thick fluid substance. I have been observing it with great care, & it really is a most curious phenomenon.—It all takes place within [one *del*, the same *added*] cell, & is, I now find certainly not from endosmose or exosmose from any *external* fluid; for a hair cut off & put *dry* between two slips of glass, shows the phenomenon splendidly. I have outline of a whole series of changes; which are infinitely varied & never cease. The movements can never be seen until after the hairs have contracted over a Fly or other substance. But I shall write a paper on the subject: so will not trouble you any more.—

[1] At the end of this letter '(going to Syria)' added in another handwriting.

You have told me what I wanted to know, whether it was some well known phenomenon.—

Yours affect
C. Darwin

Dr Bree[1] "pitches" into me handsomely.

LETTER 119

[*To: Professor Henslow*
No postmark]

15 Marine Parade Eastbourne
Oct 26th 1860

My dear Henslow

Many thanks for your note & for all the trouble about the seeds, which will be most useful to me next spring.—On my return home I will send the shillings.—I concluded that Dr Bree had blundered about the Celts. I care not for his dull unvarying abuse of me [& singular misrepresentation *added*] But at p. 244 he in fact doubts my deliberate word, and that is the act of a man who has not the soul of a gentleman in him. Kingsley[2] is "the celebrated Author & Divine" whose striking sentence I give (in 2nd Edition *added*] with his permission: I did not choose to ask

---

[1] C. R. Bree wrote *Species not Transmutable, nor the Result of Secondary Causes. Being a Critical Examination of Mr. Darwin's Work entitled 'Origin and Variation of Species'*, 1860. In *The Athenaeum* of November 1860, this book was favourably reviewed, the reviewer condemning Natural Selection as 'untenable and against religion'. This is the type of literary criticism Darwin was faced with: 'For new theorists excommunication is preferable to no communication, and for them it is better to be sent to Purgatory than to Coventry.' Dr Bree wrote of the Kingsley quotation given in the next letter: 'I confess that I have not yet fully made up my mind that any divine could have ever penned lines so fatal to the truths he is called upon to teach.' See also *LL*, II, p. 358, and *ML*, I, p. 147.

[2] In the second edition of *O*, 1860, Darwin added the following quotation from the Rev. C. Kingsley's letter, with his permission, Chap. XIV, p. 481: 'A celebrated author and divine has written to me that "he has gradually learnt to see that it is just as noble a conception of the Deity to believe that He created a few original forms capable of self-development into other and needful forms, as to believe that He required a fresh act of creation to supply the voids caused by the action of His laws".'

P

him to let me use his name, & as he did not volunteer, I had of course no choice.

I read with interest your letter in Athenaeum. Lyell seems to consider the deposits ordinary fluviatile beds, & not as showing signs of a debacle. It is the most interesting subject which Geology has turned up for many a long year.—[1]

Dr Freke[2] has sent me his paper,—which is far beyond my scope, —something like the capital quiz in the Anti-Jacobins on my Grandfather, which was quoted in the Quarterly R.ʷ My poor girl improved during the first four weeks here, but has had this last week a fearful attack, & is much exhausted, & we are much dispirited about her.—When we shall be able to take her home I cannot conjecture.

> My dear old master
> Your affect.
> C. Darwin

LETTER 120

[*To: Professor Henslow*
No postmark]

Eastbourne
Nov 10 [*1860*]

My dear Henslow.

We return home this afternoon, as my poor dear girl is now just strong enough to bear removal.—I received your letter forwarded from Down this morning, & very much obliged I am to you for

<hr>

[1] In October 1861, great interest was being aroused by C. Lyell's finds near Bedford of hand-worked flints in river-bed deposits. See also Letter 117, and *ML*, II, p. 190. In *The Athenaeum* of November 3, 1860, Henslow wrote of his difficulty in reconciling man-made hatchets found in what had been considered pre-Adamite gravels. 'We have cast off old prejudices erroneously deduced from the letter of the Scriptures, in regard to the age of the earth, but we cannot cast off our received opinions in regard to the time which man has inhabited the earth, without first feeling assured that these hatchet-bearing gravels must be several thousand years older than the Pyramids of Egypt.'

[2] Dr Freke on the 'Origin of Species by means of Organic Affinity'. See *LL*, II, p. 359.

having taken so much trouble about Dr Bree. I had thought I would have inserted a letter in some Journal on so unprovoked attack on my veracity; but I am glad I did not. No one would ever have dreamed of his interpretations. Again I sincerely thank you.—I never heard of such a muddle about the stone Hatchets. If you are sure that you can spare & know no one else who would make better use of B. de Perthes Book,[1] I sh^d like to have a copy. His course of investigations has been a strange one.—

On my return home I will settle about the seeds.—

I am still at work on Drosera. I asked you about the moving red matter in the cells, & now for the chance of your knowing, I want to ask one other question; but please *observe* if I get no answer I shall understand that you do not know.—My question is whether, observations have been made on the action of weak solutions of Carb. of Ammonia (or of other salts) on the fluid contents of the cells of living plants.—I find that C. of Ammonia has a remarkable & rapid action when absorbed by the roots.

My dear Henslow
Ever yours gratefully
C. Darwin

LETTER 121

[*To: Professor Henslow*
No postmark]

Down Bromley Kent
Dec. 10th [*1860?*]

My dear Henslow

I am exceedingly obliged for the specimens, which with your good packing came quite safe. As I sh^d have had to pay more for Box per Railway, you must let me enclose the 20 stamps.

---

[1] Jacques Boucher Crèvecoeur de Perthes, 1788–1868, French geologist and archaeologist, Director of the Douane at Abbeville. As early as 1830 he discovered flints in the gravels of the Somme valley, which he believed to be worked by man. From 1847–64, he published his *Antiquités Celtiques et antédiluviennes*, in which he first established the existence of man in the Pleistocene with remains of elephant, rhinoceros etc. See C. Lyell's *Antiquity of Man*, 1863, p. 98 et seq.

The comb of Hornet is beautiful & interests me much, for I see each is made curved on sides in lower part, until a cell is made beyond & then is built upwards hexagonally; & this just agrees with my notion.—If next year you could get me some Hornet combs *fresh* with *extreme growing margins not in the least injured,* they would be VERY valuable to me. What a pretty nest of the Vespa rufa! & how very curious the cast of Chalk bases. I sh^d like sometimes to hear, whether the *excavated* bases were covered with paper or quite bare? I sh^d really be glad to know this, & whether the little cups are [only apparent & *added*] marked merely by being separated [from each other *added*] by hexagonal reticulations, or whether each is really CONCAVE.

Will you be so kind when at Ipswich to observe this for me. I am greatly interested in these wondrous architectural Instincts.

With many thanks
Yours most sincerely
C. Darwin

BIBLIOGRAPHY

For further bibliographical detail on Darwin's writings, see R. B. Freeman's, *The Works of Charles Darwin*, an annotated bibliographical handlist.   (Dawsons of Pall Mall, 1965)

BABINGTON, C. C., *Manual of British Botany*, 1843 etc.

BADEN POWELL, The Rev., *Essays on the Spirit of the inductive philosophy and the Unity of worlds, the philosophy of Creation*, 1855.

BARLOW, Nora, *Charles Darwin and the Voyage of the Beagle*, edited with introduction by Nora Barlow. Pilot Press, 1945.

BELL, Thomas, *A History of British Reptiles*, 1839. See also Darwin, C. *Zoology of H.M.S. Beagle*, Vol. V.

BURCHELL, William John, *Travels in South Africa 1810–1815. Travels in South America, 1826–1829.*

CHALMERS, P., *Vestiges of the Natural History of Creation*, 1851.

DARWIN, Charles, *The Autobiography of Charles Darwin, 1809–1882*, with original omissions restored, edited with appendix and notes by his granddaughter Nora Barlow. Collins, London, 1958.
Bulletin of the British Museum (Natural History) Historical Series.
Darwin's Notebooks on Transmutation of Species, Vol. 2; Nos. 1, 2, 3, 4 and 5, edited by Sir Gavin de Beer, 1957. No. 6, Agenda and Corrigenda, edited by Sir Gavin de Beer and M. J. Rowlands.
Darwin's Ornithological Notes, No. 7, edited with an Introduction by Nora Barlow, 1959–63. All referred to as *Bull. B.M.(N.H.)*, Vol. 2, etc.
Cirripedia, a monograph of the sub-class Cirripedia. The Ray Society, London, 1851.
Cirripedia, fossil; a monograph of the fossil Cirripedia. Palaeontographical Society, London, 1854.

Coral Reefs, 3rd ed. (John Murray, London, 1889).
See *Geology of the Voyage* for first edition, 1842.

Charles Darwin's Diary of the Voyage of H.M.S. Beagle, edited from the MSS by Nora Barlow. Cambridge University Press, 1933.

The Different Forms of Flowers on Plants of the same Species. John Murray, 1877.

The Formation of Vegetable Mould through the action of Worms. John Murray, 1881.

The Geology of the voyage of the Beagle. Smith Elder & Co., London.
Part I   : *The Structure & distribution of coral reefs,* 1842;
Part II   : *Geological observations on the volcanic islands,* 1844;
Part III : *Geological observations on South America,* 1846.

Insectivorous Plants. John Murray, 1875.

Journal of researches, first published in 1839 as Vol. III of Captain Robert FitzRoy's 3-vol. narrative of the surveying voyages of His Majesty's ships *Adventure* and *Beagle,* 1832–6. Second edition, John Murray, 1845; Tenth thousand, John Murray, 1860, etc.

On the Origin of Species by means of Natural Selection, or the preservation of favoured races in the struggle for life. John Murray 1859.

Variation of Animals and Plants under Domestication. 2 vols., John Murray, 1868.

Zoology of the Voyage of H.M.S. Beagle, edited and superintended by Charles Darwin. Smith Elder.
Part I   : *Fossil Mammalia,* by Richard Owen, 1840;
Part II   : *Mammalia,* by George R. Waterhouse, 1839;
Part III : *Birds,* by John Gould and G. R. Gray, 1841;
Part IV : *Fish,* by Rev. Leonard Jenyns, 1842;
Part V   : *Reptiles,* by Thomas Bell, 1843.

DARWIN, Francis, *Life and Letters of Charles Darwin,* including an autobiographical chapter, edited by his son, F. Darwin. 3 vols., John Murray, 1887.

More Letters of Charles Darwin, edited by F. Darwin and A. C. Seward. 2 vols., John Murray, 1903.

DE CANDOLLE, Alphonse, *Géographie Botanique.* 2 vols., 1855.
Dictionnaire classique d'histoire naturelle. Tomes 1–17, 1822–31.

EYTON, Thomas Campbell, *Rarer Birds of Britain*. 1836.
 Catalogue of British Birds. 1838.

GOSSE, Edmund, *Life of Philip Henry Gosse*. 1890.

HOOKER, Joseph Dalton, *Himalayan Journals*. 2 vols., John Murray, 1854.
 Essay on the Flora of Tasmania. 1860.
 Handbook of New Zealand Flora.
 Flora of British Isles.

HUMBOLDT, Friedrich Heinrich Alexander, *Ansichten der Natur*, published in 1809, was largely incorporated in his later work, *Cosmos*. His travels, edited and prepared by him appeared in 30 vols., 1807–17 as *Voyages aux Régions Equinoxiales du Nouveau Continent.*

JENYNS, Reverend Leonard, *Memoir of the Reverend John Stevens Henslow*. John von Voorst, Paternoster Row, 1862.

KEITH, Arthur, *Darwin Revalued*. Watts & Co., 1955.

LITCHFIELD, H. E., *Emma Darwin. A century of Family Letters*. 2 vols.
 privately printed, Cambridge University Press, 1904
 edited by H. E. Litchfield, Darwin's daughter, John Murray, 1915.

LYELL, Charles, *Antiquity of Man*. John Murray, 1863.
 Principles of Geology, or the modern changes of the earth and its inhabitants. 1830; tenth edition. John Murray, 1867.
 Elements of Geology. An expansion of the fourth book of the *Principles*. John Murray, 1838.

MACLEAY, William Sharp, *Horae Entomologicae*. 1819–21.

MALTHUS, T. R., *An Essay on the Principles of Population*. 2 vols., 1806.

SEDGWICK, Adam, *Life and Letters of Adam Sedgwick*, by J. W. Clark and M. Hughes. 2 vols., 1890.

WHEWELL, William, *History of the Inductive Sciences.* 1837.
Philosophy of the Inductive Sciences. 1840.

YARRELL, William, *History of British Fishes.* 1835–6.
History of British Birds. 1839–43.

APPENDIX I

[Darwin's recollections of J. S. Henslow, written in 1862 and in 1873]

Darwin was asked to contribute to the *Memoir of Henslow* by Leonard Jenyns, published in 1862, and Jenyns wrote of the inclusion of Darwin's recollections: 'As it is the main object of this Memoir to set forth Professor Henslow's character in a true point of view, and to show the influence for good he exercised on others, it gives me great pleasure to be able to insert the following recollections of him from Mr. Darwin ... who could so thoroughly appreciate the excellence of his disposition.'

Darwin wrote: 'I went to Cambridge early in the year 1828, and soon became acquainted, through some of my brother entomologists, with Professor Henslow, for all who cared for any branch of natural history were equally encouraged by him. Nothing could be more simple, cordial, and unpretending than the encouragement which he afforded to all young naturalists. I soon became intimate with him, for he had a remarkable power of making the young feel completely at ease with him though we were all awe-struck with the amount of his knowledge. Before I saw him, I heard one young man sum up his attainments by simply saying that he knew everything. When I reflect how immediately we felt at perfect ease with a man older and in every way so immensely our superior, I think it was as much owing to the transparent sincerity of his character as to his kindness of heart; and, perhaps, even still more to a highly remarkable absence in him of all self-consciousness. One perceived at once that he never thought of his own varied knowledge or clear intellect, but solely on the subject in hand. Another charm, which must have struck everyone, was that his manner to old and distinguished persons and to the youngest student was exactly the the same: to all he showed the same winning courtesy. He would receive with interest the most trifling observation in any branch of natural history; and however absurd a blunder one might make, he pointed it out so clearly and kindly that one left him no way disheartened, but only determined to be more accurate the next time. In short, no man could be better formed to win the entire confidence of the young, and to encourage them in their pursuits.

'His Lectures on Botany were universally popular, and as clear as daylight. So popular were they, that several of the older members of the University attended successive courses. Once every week he kept open house in the evening, and all who cared for natural history attended these parties, which, by thus favouring intercommunication, did the same good in Cambridge, in a very pleasant manner, as the Scientific Societies do in London. At these parties many of the most distinguished members of the University occasionally attended; and when only a few were present, I have listened to the great men of those days, conversing on all sorts of subjects, with the most varied and brilliant powers. This was no small advantage to some of the younger men, as it stimulated their mental activity and ambition. Two or three times in each session he took excursions with his botanical class; either a long walk to the habitat of some rare plant, or in a barge down the river to the fens, or in coaches to some more distant place, as to Gamlingay, to see the wild lily of the valley, and to catch on the heath the rare natter-jack. These excursions have left a delightful impression on my mind. He was, on such occasions, in as good spirits as a boy, and laughed as heartily as a boy at the misadventures of those who chased the splendid swallow-tail butterflies across the broken and treacherous fens. He used to pause every now and then and lecture on some plant or other object; and something he could tell us on every insect, shell, or fossil collected, for he had attended to every branch of natural history. After our day's work we used to dine at some inn or house, and most jovial we then were. I believe all who joined these excursions will agree with me that they have left an enduring impression of delight on our minds.

'As time passed on at Cambridge I became very intimate with

Professor Henslow, and his kindness was unbounded; he continually asked me to his house, and allowed me to accompany him in his walks. He talked on all subjects, including his deep sense of religion, and was entirely open. I owe more than I can express to this excellent man. His kindness was steady: when Captain Fitzroy offered to give up part of his own cabin to any naturalist who would join the expedition in H.M.S. Beagle, Professor Henslow recommended me, as one who knew very little, but who, he thought, would work. I was strongly attached to natural history, and this attachment I owed, in large part, to him. During the five years' voyage, he regularly corresponded with me and guided my efforts; he received, opened, and took care of all the specimens sent home in many large boxes; but I firmly believe that, during these five years, it never once crossed his mind that he was acting towards me with unusual and generous kindness.

'During the years when I associated so much with Professor Henslow, I never once saw his temper even ruffled. He never took an ill-natured view of anyone's character, though very far from blind to the foibles of others. It always struck me that his mind could not be even touched by any paltry feeling of vanity, envy, or jealousy. With all this equability of temper and remarkable benevolence, there was no insipidity of character. A man must have been blind not to have perceived that beneath this placid exterior there was a vigorous and determined will. When principle came into play, no power on earth could have turned him one hair's breadth.

'After the year 1842, when I left London, I saw Professor Henslow only at long intervals; but to the last, he continued in all respects the same man. I think he cared somewhat less about science, and more for his parishioners. When speaking of his allotments, his parish children, and plans of amusing and instructing them, he would always kindle up with interest and enjoyment. I remember one trifling fact which seemed to me highly characteristic of the man: in one of the bad years for the potato, I asked him how his crop had fared; but after a little talk I perceived that, in fact, he knew nothing about his own potatoes, but seemed to know exactly what sort of crop there was in the garden of almost every poor man in his parish. [See Letter 66, p. 156.]

'In intellect, as far as I could judge, accurate powers of observation, sound sense, and cautious judgement seemed predominant. Nothing seemed to give him so much enjoyment, as drawing conclusions from minute observations. But his admirable memoir on the geology of Anglesea, shows his capacity for extended observations and broad views. Reflecting over his character with gratitude and reverence, his moral attributes rise, as they should do in the highest character, in pre-eminence over his intellect.

C. Darwin.'

More than ten years later, in 1873, when writing his *Autobiography*, Darwin again recorded his memories of his old friend, but in a manner more warmly intimate than he had done for Jenyn's *Memoir*. I give the passages here, as an integral part in the dual portrayal of their personalities.

'I have not as yet mentioned a circumstance which influenced my whole career more than any other. This was my friendship with Prof. Henslow. Before coming up to Cambridge, I had heard of him from my brother as a man who knew every branch of science, and I was accordingly prepared to reverence him. He kept open house once every week, where all undergraduates and several older members of the University, who were attached to science, used to meet in the evening. I soon got, through Fox, an invitation, and went there regularly. Before long I became well acquainted with Henslow, and during the latter half of my time at Cambridge took long walks with him on most days; so that I was called by some of the dons "the man who walks with Henslow"; and in the evening I was very often asked to join his family dinner. His knowledge was great in botany, entomology, chemistry, mineralogy, and geology. His strongest taste was to draw conclusions from long-continued minute observations. His judgement was excellent, and his whole mind well-balanced; but

I do not suppose that anyone would say that he possessed much original genius.

'He was deeply religious, and so orthodox, that he told me one day he should be grieved if a single word of the Thirty-nine Articles were altered. His moral qualities were in every way admirable. He was free from every tinge of vanity or other petty feeling; and I never saw a man who thought so little about himself or his own concerns. His temper was imperturbably good, with the most winning and courteous manners; yet, as I have seen, he could be roused by any bad action to the warmest indignation and prompt action. I once saw in his company in the streets of Cambridge almost as horrid a scene as could have been witnessed during the French Revolution. Two body-snatchers had been arrested and whilst being taken to prison had been torn from the constable by a crowd of the roughest men, who dragged them by their legs along the muddy and stony road. They were covered from head to foot with mud and their faces were bleeding either from having been kicked or from the stones; they looked like corpses, but the crowd was so dense that I got only a few momentary glimpses of the wretched creatures. Never in my life have I seen such wrath painted on a man's face, as was shown by Henslow at this horrid scene. He tried repeatedly to penetrate the mob; but it was simply impossible. He then rushed away to the mayor, telling me not to follow him, to get more policemen. I forget the issue, except that the two were got into the prison before being killed.

'Henslow's benevolence was unbounded, as he proved by his many excellent schemes for his poor parishioners, when in after years he held the living of Hitcham. My intimacy with such a man ought to have been and I hope was an inestimable benefit. I cannot resist mentioning a trifling incident which showed his kind consideration. Whilst examining some pollen-grains on a damp surface I saw the tubes exserted, and instantly rushed off to communicate my surprising discovery to him. Now I do not suppose any other Professor of Botany could have helped laughing at my coming in such a hurry to make such a communication. But he agreed how interesting the phenomenon was, and explained its meaning, but made me clearly understand how well it was known; so I left him not in the least mortified, but well pleased at having discovered for myself so remarkable a fact, but determined not to be in such a hurry again to communicate my discoveries.'

Henslow's great influence was mainly anonymous. But the Rev. W. A. Leighton, Darwin's friend at Cambridge and senior by four years, paid this tribute to him when he wrote his *Flora of Shropshire* in 1841, dedicated to Henslow in these words: 'These simple fruits of his labours are dedicated by his grateful pupil W. A. Leighton.' My attention to this dedication was drawn by Sir Edward Salisbury, F.R.S., whose help at other stages in preparing these letters for the Press, I should like here to record.

W. A. Leighton also wrote the *Lichen-Flora of Great Britain and the Channel Islands*, published 1871.

APPENDIX II

The five quarto volumes of the *Zoology of the Beagle*, which
Darwin edited and superintended, were issued in the years 1839
to 1843 and involved heavy work and much journeying to London. The volumes on the *Geology of the Voyage*, his major interest and study during the years of travel, ran currently with the
last volume of the *Zoology*, and came out in 1842, 1844 and 1846.
More important as evidence of his maturing evolutionary thought
are the two manuscript sketches on evolution of 1842 and 1844,
first published in *Foundations of the Origin of Species*, 1909, edited
by Francis Darwin; and in 1959 in *Evolution by Natural Selection*,
edited by Sir Gavin de Beer. In 1845 Darwin revised his *Journal
of Researches* for Murray's edition.

In 1846 he embarked on his enormous self-imposed task of the
detailed study of the Cirripedes, or barnacles, which absorbed
him for eight years, and which appeared in four Monographs,
two in 1851, and two in 1854 (see Letters 68 and 69). Darwin
summed up his own contradictory verdict of the work's value in
his *Autobiography*, p. 118, where, late in life, he says: 'The Cirripedes form a highly varying and difficult group of species to
class; and my work was of considerable use to me, when I had to
discuss in *The Origin of Species* the principles of a natural classification. *Nevertheless, I doubt whether the work was worth the consumption of so much time.*' Let no one agree too readily with this
last sentence of Darwin's, which I have here italicised. Perhaps
the lapse of nearly thirty years had dimmed the urge that had
driven him to the undertaking. Already in 1842 he was well
advanced in his evolutionary theory which was to alter all existing beliefs on the species question, without ever having had a
detailed drilling in the morphology and physiology of any biological group, so essential to any classificatory system. Just as

he had known how to make use of every opportunity offered him on the voyage of the *Beagle*, so at this later stage in 1846 he accepted the self-imposed challenge of the vast labour of the classification of the Cirripedes so that he might feel inwardly armed for his work on the origin of species.

Immediately after the Cirripedes were off his mind, he began to collect and collate his large accumulation of material on species, and in 1856 began to plan a large work in which all references were to be included. But this project had to be superseded after the receipt in 1858 of A. R. Wallace's paper, containing an evolutionary explanation of species formation on a natural selection basis, closely resembling Darwin's own evolutionary sketch of 1844. Their papers were jointly read at a meeting of the Linnean Society in 1858, and Darwin summarised the longer work already begun in 1856 into the single famous volume *On the Origin of Species*, published in November, 1859.

Dr Robert Stauffer's recent work on the Darwin documents in the Cambridge University Library, especially on the larger work mentioned above which had to be abandoned, has thrown much light on Darwin's careful scrutiny of all arguments and references to sources, before the hastened publication of *On the Origin of Species* in November, 1859.[1] In the work of Dr Sydney Smith in his discussion in *Impulse* on 'The Origin of the Origin', and in his important analysis of the annotations in the books from Darwin's library,[2] one common point emerges, a matter that has also received frequent confirmation in Sir Gavin de Beer's work on the early Darwin notebooks:[3] namely this documentation of his developing thought constantly reveals an active germ of an idea at a date earlier than had been suspected. In the letters in this volume, Part I, 1831–8, there are abundant examples of this early build-up of ideas; and in Part II, 1838–60, we get a clear picture in Letters 81, 82, 83 and 86, of how his arguments on the greater

[1] Dr Robert Clinton Stauffer, *Science*, Vol. 130, 1959, pp. 1449–52; *Proc. Am. Phil. Soc.*, Vol. 104, No. 2, April 1960.
[2] Dr Sydney Smith, *Impulse*, Nov. 1959, pp. 2–4; *Advancement of Science*, No. 64, 1960, pp. 391–401.
[3] Sir Gavin de Beer, M. J. Rowlands and others, *Bull. B.M.* (*N.H.*), Vol. II.

variation and wider geographical range in species of larger genera than in species of small genera were reached. This argument appears in Chapter II of *The Origin*, but in the early draft was to have had a chapter to itself.

In the main, Darwin's theory played little part in his correspondence with Henslow after 1840, and the record of Darwin's major works given in this Appendix from 1839–61 has little echo in the letters. The intense concentration of effort in their creation lay outside the reach of this long-enduring friendship.

APPENDIX III

[This advice to collectors, taken from 'Journal of Researches', 1839, pp. 598–602, gives Darwin's considered opinion on the procedure that should be followed, learnt from his own experience. These passages were not included in later editions of the 'Journal of Researches'. In 'A Manual of Scientific enquiry prepared for the use of Her Majesty's Navy and adapted for travellers in general', edited by Sir John Herschel, Bart, 1849, some of the same advice is given. The quoted passages show Darwin's keen insight into essentials, besides revealing some of the difficulties of scientific collecting in the days of sailing vessels.]

'As this volume may possibly fall into the hands of some one about to undertake a similar expedition, I will offer a few pieces of advice, some of which I observed with much advantage, but others, to my cost, neglected. Let the collector's motto be, "Trust nothing to the memory"; for the memory becomes a fickle guardian when one interesting object is succeeded by another still more interesting. Keep a list with the date of the ships by which *every* box of specimens, or even a letter, is transmitted to England; let the receiver do the same: it will afterwards save much anxiety. Put a number on every specimen, and every fragment of a specimen; and during the very same minute let it be entered in the catalogue, so that if hereafter its locality be doubted, the collector may say in good truth, "every specimen of mine was ticketed on the spot". Anything which is folded up in paper, or put into a separate box, ought to have a number on the outside (with the exception perhaps of geological specimens), but more *especially* a duplicate number on the inside attached to the specimen itself. A series of small numbers should be printed from 0 to 5000; a stop must be added to those numbers which can be read upside down (as 699. or 86.). It is likewise convenient to have the different thousands printed on differently coloured paper, so that when unpacking a single glance tells the approximate number.

'For specimens in spirits of wine, I found the following plan answered admirably: Get a set of steel dies from o to 9, a small punch, and some sheets of *trebly*-thick tinfoil. The numbers may at any time be stamped in a line, with a hole punched in front of each, and then cut off with a pair of scissors as wanted. These tickets cost little trouble in making, and *do not corrode*. Each specimen in spirits should be loosely folded up in a *very open* gauze, or some such stuff; the string which ties up the corners may likewise secure the number. Use nothing but glass jars; but these are difficult to be obtained of any size out of Europe. Jars of earthenware, and wooden casks, either leak, or allow of evaporation; and when such are used, it is not easy to know whether the specimens are too much crowded (a very common fault), or in what state the spirit is in, which through glass can be judged of by its colour. Bear in mind, that in nine out of ten specimens which are spoiled it is owing to the spirit being too weak. The jars should be closed with a bung covered by bladder, twice by common tinfoil, and by bladder again; let the bladder soak till half putrid. I found this plan quite worth the trouble it cost.

'Few, excepting those who have travelled in ships, know the extreme inconvenience of want of room; and on this much depends: but if it be practicable, keep three or four sets of bottles open at the same time so that one may serve for crustacea, another for animals for dissection, another for minute specimens, another for fish, always putting the latter into the strongest spirit. Anyhow, it is absolutely necessary to keep a couple of receiving bottles in which everything can at first be put, and afterwards transferred to the permanent bottles with *fresh spirits*. Without assistance from government, and plenty of room, it is most disheartening work to attempt to bring home many specimens in spirits, although without doubt in such a state they are very far the most valuable. I should recommend anyone circumstanced as I was to preserve the skins only of large fish and reptiles. But with room and means at command let the collector place no limit to the number of his glass jars.

'With respect to the catalogues, it is inconvenient to have many; but there must at least be two, one for the tin labels or specimens in spirits, and another for the paper numbers, which should be applied indiscriminately to every kind of specimen. If the observer has any particular branch to which he devotes much attention, a third catalogue exclusively for such specimens is desirable: I kept a third for geological specimens and fossils. In a like manner notes should be as simple as possible: I kept one set for geology, and another for zoological and all other observations. It is well to endeavour to write upon separate pages remarks on different specimens; for much copying will thus be saved. My journal was likewise kept distinct from the other subjects. I found an arrangement carried thus far very useful: a traveller by land would, I suppose, be obliged to adopt a still more simple plan.

'Use arsenical soap[1] for all skins, but do not neglect to brush the legs and beak with a solution of corrosive sublimate. Likewise slightly brush over all dried plants with the solution. For collecting insects use a plain strong sweeping-net, and pack the specimens of all orders, excepting lepidoptera, between layers of rag in pill-boxes, placing at the bottom a bit of camphor; this costs *scarcely any* trouble, and the insects, especially thousands of unknown minute ones, arrive in an excellent state. Take a good stock of chip pill-boxes—a simple plain strong microscope, such as that long ago described by Ellis—a good stock of lace-needles, with glass tubes and sealingwax, for the purpose of making dissecting instruments. I need not mention small collecting bottles covered with leather, tin boxes, dissecting scissors, blowpipe case, compasses, mountain barometer, etc. I should recommend a sort of work-box fitted up to hold watch-glasses, glass micrometers, pins, string, printed numbers, etc.; and I found a small cabinet with drawers, some lined with cork, and others with cross partitions, most useful as a temporary storehouse.

'Pack up for shipment *every* specimen of *every* kind in boxes lined with tinned plates, and *soldered* together: if the case be large the specimens should further be packed into light pasteboard or

[1] 'Seeds must not be sent home in the same case with skins prepared with poison, camphor, or essential oils; scarcely any of mine germinated, and Professor Henslow thinks they were thus killed.'

other boxes, for by long pressure even skins of quadrupeds are injured. On no account whatever put bottles with spirits of wine, though ever so well packed, in the same case with other specimens, for if one should break everything near it will be spoiled, as I found to my cost in one instance.

'When limited either in time, funds, or space, let not the collector crowd too many specimens either into one bottle, or into one case. For he should *constantly* bear in mind as his second motto, that "It is better to send home a few things well preserved, than a multitude in a bad condition." As long as due steps are taken that the harvest may not be spoiled, let him not be disheartened, because he may for a long time be labouring by himself; let him work hard from morning to night, for every day and every hour is precious in a foreign clime; and then most assuredly his own satisfaction will one day well repay him.'

APPENDIX IV

*[A note on Charles Darwin and Coral Islands
by D. R. Stoddart]*

Darwin's interest in corals during the early part of the voyage was clearly zoological, and it was not until he found impressive evidence of crustal movement in the Andes that he began to form his theory of the development of barrier reefs and atolls by slow subsidence of the reef foundations. This was first mentioned in a field notebook in July 1835, (see *Charles Darwin and the Voyage of the Beagle* by Nora Barlow, 1945, pp. 243–4) and written out in full as a separate paper in December 1835 ('C. Darwin: *Coral Islands*', edited by D. R. Stoddart, *Atoll Research Bulletin* 88, 1962). After the voyage Darwin expanded the theory into a book on *The structure and distribution of coral reefs* (1842), which is the definitive statement of his theory. Darwin stressed the fact that reef corals can only live in shallow water, and where reefs rise from deep water, they can only be explained by subsidence of the foundations, with the corals keeping pace by upward growth. This implies that thicknesses of reef limestone greatly exceeding the depth at which corals can grow may develop in such places. Deep borings in reefs to test Darwin's theory have shown 1,114 ft of reef limestone at Funafuti, 2,556 ft at Bikini and 4,610 ft at Eniwetok, the latter cores ending in oceanic basalts as Darwin's theory would predict, and the whole column of limestone being formed of shallow-water organisms. These results strikingly confirmed Darwin's views for deep-ocean atolls, and further evidence has come from seismic and gravity studies in the Gilbert, Ellice and Marshall Islands; from the dredging of volcanic rocks from great depths on atoll slopes in the Marshall and Tuamotu Islands; and from the discovery of drowned seamounts in the Pacific, some capped by fossil corals, which presumably subsided too rapidly for the growing corals to keep pace with them. For deep-ocean reefs, Darwin's theory is thus strikingly confirmed. For barrier reefs in continental areas, however, the problem is more complex, and coastal faulting as well as subsidence must be considered. The chief factor neglected by Darwin was the shifts of sea level caused by the Pleistocene glaciations, which at one time were used as the basis for an alternative 'glacial control theory' of coral reefs. Glacial control, however, is now seen as a relatively minor factor influencing surface characteristics of reefs and as supplementary to Darwin's theory, augmenting rather than replacing it.

APPENDIX V

List of Letters

[Letters are from Charles Darwin to John Stevens Henslow unless otherwise stated. The main sources are given. Kew Library (K.L.), and Cambridge University Library (C.U.L.). 'Pamphlet' refers to the Cambridge Philosophical Society's pamphlet of 1835. Previously printed letters are marked by an asterisk, those partly printed by a dagger; unmarked letters have not to my knowledge been published before. The abbreviations of the printed sources may be found on p. 24.]

PART I

1†	K.L.	(*LL*, I, pp. 189–90)	Shrewsbury	11 Jul. 1831
2†	C.U.L.	G. Peacock to J. S. Henslow (*LL*, I, pp. 191–2)	7 Suffolk St, Pall Mall East	[*Before 24 Aug*] 1831
3*	C.U.L.	J. S. Henslow to Charles Darwin (*LL*, I, pp. 192–3)	Cambridge	24 Aug. 1831
4†	C.U.L.	G. Peacock to Charles Darwin (*LL*, I, pp. 193–4)		n.d.
5†	K.L.	(*LL*, I, pp. 195–6)	Shrewsbury	30 Aug. 1831
6*	C.U.L.	Charles Darwin to Dr R. Darwin (*LL*, I, pp. 196–7)	[*Maer*]	31 Aug. 1831
7*	C.U.L.	Josiah Wedgwood to Dr R. Darwin (*LL*, I, pp. 198–9)	Maer	31 Aug. 1831
8*	K.L.	(*LL*, I, p. 199)	Cambridge	Aug. 1831 [*A mistake for Sept. 2*]
9*	K.L.	(*LL*, I, pp. 203–4)	[*17 Spring Gardens, London*]	Sept. 1831 [*Postmark Sept. 5*]
10	K.L.		17 Spring Gardens	9 Sept. 1831
11	K.L.		17 Spring Gardens	17 Sept. 1831
12	K.L.		[*Shrewsbury*]	28 Sept. 1831
13	K.L.		17 Spring Gardens	18 Oct. 1831
14	C.U.L.	J. S. Henslow to Charles Darwin	Cambridge	25 Oct. 1831

15	K.L.		4 Clarence Baths, Devonport	30 Oct. 1831
16†	K.L.	(*LL*, I, pp. 214–15)	Devonport	15 Nov. 1831
17	C.U.L.	J. S. Henslow to Charles Darwin	Cambridge	20 Nov. 1831
18†	K.L.	(*LL*, I, p. 216)	Devonport	3 Dec. 1831
19†	K.L.	(*LL*, I, p. 235 and Pamphlet)	Rio de Janeiro	18 May 1832
20*	K.L.	(*ML*, I, pp. 8–10 and Pamphlet)	Monte Video	15 Aug. 1832
21*	K.L.	(*ML*, I, pp. 11–14 and Pamphlet)	Monte Video	24 Nov. 1832
22	C.U.L.	J. S. Henslow to Charles Darwin	Cambridge	15 Jan. 1832 [*should be 1833*]
23	K.L.	Erasmus Darwin to J. S. Henslow	24 Regent St	23 Jan. 1833
24	K.L.	Dr & Miss Darwins to J. S. Henslow	Shrewsbury	1 Feb. 1833
25	C.U.L.	Dr R. Darwin to Charles Darwin	[*Shrewsbury*]	7 Mar. 1833
26†	K.L.	(*LL*, I, pp. 242–4 and Pamphlet)	[*At Sea*]	11 Apr. 1833
27†	K.L.	(Pamphlet)	Rio de la Plata	18 July 1833
28	C.U.L.	J. S. Henslow to Charles Darwin	Cambridge	31 Aug. 1833
29	K.L.		Buenos Ayres	Sept. 1833
30†	K.L.	(Pamphlet)	Monte Video	12 Nov. 1833
31†	K.L.	(*LL*, I, pp. 249–51)	E. Falkland Island	Mar. 1834
32	K.L.	Edward Lumb to J. S. Henslow	Buenos Ayres	2 May 1834
33	C.U.L.	J. S. Henslow to Charles Darwin	Cholsey, near Wallingford	22 July 1834
4*	K.L.	(*ML*, I, pp. 14–20)	Valparaiso	24 July 1834
	K.L.		Valparaiso	4 Oct. 1834
	K.L.		Valparaiso	8 Nov. 1834
	K.L.	(Pamphlet)	[*Valparaiso*]	Mar. 1835
	K.L.	(*ML*, I, pp. 20–5 and Pamphlet)	Valparaiso	18 Apr. 1835
	.L.	(*ML*, I, pp. 26–7)	Lima	12 July 1835
	.L.	Dr Darwin to J. S. Henslow	Shrewsbury	28 Dec. 1835
		(*LL*, I, pp. 264–5)	Sydney	Jan. 1836

42†	K.L.	(*LL*, I, pp. 267–8)	St Helena	9 July 1836
43*	K.L.	(*LL*, I, p. 269)	Shrewsbury	6 Oct. 1836
44†	K.L.	(*LL*, I, p. 273)	43 Great Marl-borough St [*London*]	30 Oct. 1836
45†	K.L.	(*LL*, I, p. 275)	43 Great Marl-borough St	[*2 Nov. 1836*]
46	K.L.		36 Great Marl-borough St	28 Mar. 1837
47†	K.L.	(*LL*, I, p. 283)	36 Great Marl-borough St	18 May 1837
48	K.L.			28 May 1837
49	K.L.		36 Great Marl-borough St	14 July 1837
50	K.L.		36 Great Marl-borough St	Aug. 1837
51	K.L.		36 Great Marl-borough St	16 Aug. 1837
52†	K.L.	(*LL*, I, p. 284)	36 Great Marl-borough St	20 Sept. 1837
53	K.L.			23 Sept. 1837
54†	K.L.	(*LL*, I, pp. 285–7)		14 Oct. 1837
55†	K.L.	(*LL*, I, p. 288)		[*4 Nov. 1837*]
56	K.L.			21 Nov. 1837

PART II

57	C.U.L.		36 Great Marl-borough St	[*26 Mar. 1838*]
58	C.U.L.	J. S. Henslow to Charles Darwin	Cambridge	16 Dec. 1838
59	C.U.L.			26 Jan. 1840
60	C.U.L.		Shrewsbury	3 July 1840
61	C.U.L.			18 Sept. [*1842?*]
62†	C.U.L.	(*ML*, II, p. 244, footnote)	Down, Bromley, Kent	8 Sept. 1843
63	C.U.L.		Shrewsbury	14 Oct. 1843
64†	C.U.L.	(*ML*, II, pp. 245–6)	Down	5 Nov. 1843
65†	C.U.L.	(*LL*, I, p. 343)	Down	25 July 1845
66	American Phil. Soc. Philadelphia		Down	28 Oct. 1845

67	C.U.L.		Down	6 Oct. 1846
68†	C.U.L.	(*ML*, I, pp. 61–2)	Down	1 Apr. 1848
69	C.U.L.		Down	2 July [*1848*]
70†	C.U.L.	(*ML*, I, pp. 66–7)	The Lodge, Malvern	6 May 1849
71	C.U.L.		Down	[*After 21 Sept. 1849*]
72	C.U.L.		Down	17 Jan [*1850*]
73	C.U.L.		Down	[*1850 or '51?*]
74	C.U.L.			[*1850 or '51?*]
75	C.U.L.		Down	8 Mar. [*1853*]
76	C.U.L.		Down	31 Mar. [*1853?*]
77	C.U.L.		Down	11 Dec. [*1853?*]
78	American Phil. Soc. Philadelphia		Down	17 Nov. [*1854*]
79	C.U.L.		Down	13 Mar. 1855
80	C.U.L.		Down	26 Mar. 1855
81	C.U.L.		Down	27 June 1855
82†	C.U.L.	(*ML*, I, p. 419)	Down	2 July 1855
83	C.U.L.		Down	7 July 1855
84	C.U.L.		Down	11 July 1855
85	C.U.L.		Down	14 July 1855
86	C.U.L.		Down	21 July [*1855*]
87	C.U.L.		Down	23 July 1855
88	C.U.L.		Down	28 July 1855
89	C.U.L.		Down	23 [*Aug.–Sept. 1855?*]
90	C.U.L.		Down	12 Oct. [*1855?*]
91	C.U.L.		Down	29 Oct. [*1855*]
92	C.U.L.		Down	10 Nov. [*1855*]
93	C.U.L.		Down	18 Dec. 1855
94	C.U.L.		Down	26 Dec. 1855
95	C.U.L.		Down	3 Jan. [*1856*]
96	C.U.L.		Down	22 Jan. [*1856*]
97	C.U.L.		Down	16 June [*1856?*]
98	C.U.L.	[*Incomplete letter*]		[*1856*]
99	C.U.L.		Down	6 Aug. 1856
	C.U.L.	[*Unplaced note*]		[*1856?*]
100	C.U.L.		Down	10 Aug. [*1857?*]
101	C.U.L.		Down	14 Oct. [*1857?*]
102	C.U.L.		Down	18 Oct. 1857
103	C.U.L.		Down	25 Jan. 1858

104	C.U.L.		Norfolk House, Shanklin, I.O.W.	4 Aug. 1858
105	C.U.L.		Down	25 Sept. [*1858?*]
106	C.U.L.		Down	9 Nov. 1858
107*		(*LL*, II, p. 217–18)	Down	11 Nov. 1859
108	C.U.L.		Down	3 Feb. 1860
109	C.U.L.		Down	9 Feb. 1860
110	C.U.L.		Down	2 Apr. 1860
111	C.U.L.	J. S. Henslow to Charles Darwin	7 Downing Terr., Cambridge	5 May 1860
112†	C.U.L.		Down	8 May [*1860*]
113†	C.U.L.	J. S. Henslow to Sir Joseph Hooker (L. Huxley's *Life of Hooker*, Vol. I, p. 512)	7 Downing Terr.	10 May 1860
114†	C.U.L.	(*ML*, I, pp. 150–1)	Down	14 May 1860
115	C.U.L.		Down	17 May [*1860*]
116	C.U.L.		at Miss Wedgwood's, Hartfield, Tonbridge Wells	16 July [*1860*]
117	C.U.L.		15 Marine Parade, Eastbourne	28 Sept. 1860
118	C.U.L.		15 Marine Parade	11 Oct. [*1860*]
119†	C.U.L.	(*ML*, I, p. 174)	15 Marine Parade	26 Oct. 1860
120	C.U.L.		Eastbourne	10 Nov. [*1860*]
121	C.U.L.		Down	10 Dec. [*1860?*]

APPENDIX VI

Itinerary of the voyage of H.M.S. *Beagle* from Dec. 18, 1832 to Dec. 2, 1836.

Dates of arrival and departure from the ports of call are given; the periods on land when the main collections of specimens were made can thus roughly be compared with the weeks at sea, when the material was examined and written up.

LEFT	ARRIVED	AT SEA	ON LAND
Devonport, Dec. 27, 1831	Cape Verde Is., Jan. 18, 1832	21 days	21 days
C. Verde Is., Feb. 8, 1832	Bahia, Brazil, Feb. 28	20 days	19 days
Bahia, Brazil, Mar. 18	Rio de Janeiro, Apr. 5	18 days	3 months
Rio de Janeiro, Jul. 5	Monte Video, Jul. 26	21 days	24 days
Monte Video, Aug. 19	Bahia Blanca, Sept. 6	18 days	41 days
Bahia Blanca, Oct. 17	Monte Video, Nov. 2	16 days	24 days
Monte Video, Nov. 26	T. del Fuego, Dec. 16	20 days	72 days
T. del Fuego, Feb. 26, 1833	Falkland Is., Mar. 1	3 days	35 days
Falkland Is., Apr. 6	Maldonado (near Monte Video), Apr. 28	22 days	56 days
Maldonado, Jul. 23	Rio Negro, Aug. 3	11 days	4 months

LEFT	ARRIVED	AT SEA	ON LAND
Monte Video, Dec. 6, 1833	Port Desire, Dec. 23	17 days	12 days
Port Desire, Jan. 4, 1834	Port St Julien (110 miles south), Jan. 9	5 days	10 days
Port St Julien, Jan. 19	Str. of Magellan (via Falkland Is.), Jan. 29	10 days	9 days
Str. of Magellan, Mar. 7	Falkland Is., Mar. 10	3 days	28 days
Falkland Is., Apr. 7	Santa Cruz River, Apr. 13	6 days	29 days
Santa Cruz, May 12	Chiloe, Jun. 28 (Many landings in Straits)	47 days	15 days
Chiloe, Jul. 13	Valparaiso, Jul. 31	18 days	102 days
Valparaiso, Nov. 10 (Illness)	Chiloe, Nov. 21	11 days	75 days
Chiloe, Feb. 4, 1835	Valdivia, Feb. 8	4 days	14 days
Valdivia, Feb. 22	Concepcion, Mar. 4 (Earthquake)	10 days	3 days
Concepcion, Mar. 7	Valparaiso, Mar. 11 (S. Jago)	4 days	117 days
Copiapò, Jul. 6	Iquiqi, Jul. 12	6 days	3 days
Iquiqui, Jul. 15	Gallao, for Lima, Jul. 19	4 days	50 days
Gallao, Sept. 7	Galapagos, Sept. 16	9 days	34 days

LEFT	ARRIVED	AT SEA	ON LAND
Galapagos, Oct. 20	Tahiti, Nov.15	26 days	11 days
Tahiti, Nov. 26	New Zealand, Dec. 21 (Bay of Islands)	26 days	9 days
New Zealand, Dec. 30	Sydney, Jan. 12, 1836	13 days	18 days
Sydney, Jan. 30	Hobart, Tasmania, Feb. 2	3 days	15 days
Hobart, Feb. 17	St George's Sound, Australia, Mar. 3	14 days	11 days
St George's Sound, Mar. 14	Keeling I., Apr. 2	19 days	10 days
Keeling I., Apr. 12	Mauritius, Apr. 29	17 days	11 days
Mauritius, May 9	C. of Good Hope, May 31	22 days	18 days
C. of Good Hope, Jun. 18	St Helena, Jul. 7	19 days	7 days
St Helena, Jul. 14	Ascencion, Jul. 19	5 days	4 days
Ascencion, Jul. 23	Bahia, Brazil, Aug. 1	9 days	5 days
Bahia, Brazil, Aug. 6	Pernambuco, Aug. 12	6 days	5 days
Pernambuco, Aug. 17	Porto Praya, C. Verde Is., Sept. 4	18 days	16 days
Terceira, Azores, Sept. 20	Falmouth, Oct. 2, 1836	12 days	

INDEX

Albrolhos, 54 and n.3, 58

Admiralty, the, and the appointment to the *Beagle*, 31, 32; and FitzRoy's survey, 60 n.

Africa, South, 114 n., 137, 243

Agassiz, Jean Louis (1807–73), 27 n.2

America, South, 10–12, 48, 55

American Philosophical Society, 156, 172 n.

Andes, the, 12, 86, 96, 102, map; D.'s expedition to, 92 and n.2, 93; evidence from shells, 96, 101; geology of, 93, 95–6, 102–7, 109–10, 234; the great lakes, 92 n.2; metallic veins, 106; plants and seeds from, 107–8; petrified trees, 105–6; Portillo pass, 102, 104; Puquenas pass, 104; Red Snow, 107; the Uspallata, 102, 105

Armadillos, 61 and n.

Armstrong, Dr, 89

Arnott, George Arnott Walker, *British Flora*, 177 and n.

Ascension Island, 115, 243

Athenaeum, The, H.'s letter on man-made hatchets, 214 and n.1

Australia, D. in, 112–14, 243

Azores, the, 116, 243; plants from, 177 and n., 180

Babington, Charles Cardale, biog., 152 n.; and the Atriplex plant, 153; naming of species, 174, 179, 183, 201

Bahia, 55, 57, 241; geological importance of St Peter and St Paul's Rocks, 54 and n.1, 66

Beagle, H.M.S., arrival in Falmouth, 117; D.'s description of, 48–9; D.'s life on board, 53, 54, 56, 63, 71; influence of voyage on his character, 8, 10; last stages of voyage, 115–17; leaves Str. of Magellan, 94; outline of voyage, 48, 241–3; position offered to D., 1–3, 19, 29–30; returns to England, 12–13, 117; off S. America, 1832–5, 10–12; sails for Galapagos Is., 109; *see also* under Darwin, Charles

Beaufort, Capt. (later Rear-Adm.) Francis (1774–1857), 28 n.1, 70; and the appointment to the *Beagle*, 31, 37, 38, 42; letter from H. to, 40 n.4

Bell, Thomas, biog., 122 n.3; *Reptiles*, 122 n.3, 123, 125, 134 n.2

Benefit Clubs, 167 and n.1, 190–1

Berkeley, Rev. Miles Joseph (1803–89), and D.'s fungus, 128 n.1

Blyth, Edward (1810–73), his influence on D., 62 n.2

Bree, C. R., and *The Origin of Species*, 213 and n.1, 215

British Association, D. and, 163 and n.1; Henslow and, 65; meetings of: Cambridge (1833), 77 and n., 86 and n.2; Liverpool (1837), 135 n.2; Southampton (1846), 158 and n.1; Oxford (1847), 160 and n.2; Birmingham (1849), 164 and n.2; Glasgow (1855), 188 and n.; Cheltenham (1856), 194 n.1; Oxford (1860), 209 n.1; *Whewell* and, 87 n.

British Museum, 46, 119, 125, 135

Broderip, William John (1789–1859), and D.'s shells, 123

Brown, Robert, biog., 125 n.1; and D.'s plants and fossil woods, 125, 127–8, 128 n.1, 130, 132, 135; use of lenses, 42 and n.2, 44

Burchell, William John, biog., 38 n.

Buckland, Rev. William, and British Association, 77 n.; and D.'s specimens, 120

Buenos Ayres, 64; D.'s land crossing to, 81, 82

Butler, Samuel (1774–1839), headmaster of Shrewsbury, 1

Cambridge, H.'s involvement in borough politics, 45 and n., 65

Cambridge Philosophical Society, xi, xii, 46; D. on Viviparous Lizards, 107 n.2; and D.'s work, 147, 203, 204; its formation, 4

Cambridge University, D. and, 1, 4, 52; establishment of Natural Science Tripos, 6; first Botanic Garden, 5; H. and the study of natural history, 4, 5–7, 211–212

Canada, lumber duties in, 155

Canary Islands, D.'s plan to visit, 2, 25, 26, 27, 40 n.4

Cape Horn, 61, 71

Cape of Good Hope, 111, 113, 116, 243; its Royal Observatory, 116 n.

Cape Tres Montes, 98

Cape Verde Islands, 48, 241; D. and, 10–11, 53 and n.1, 116

Carcarana river, 82

Carlyle, Thomas (1795–1881), *Reminiscences*, 13

Cauquenes, its Hot Baths, 97

Chagas Disease, D. and, 96 *n*.2

Chagos Lagoon, 149

Chili, 82; evidence of recent ocean covering, 96; geology of, 100–1, 102–7, 110; its naturalists, 97

Chiloe Island, its *Berberis darwinii*, 95 *n*.; geology of, 101, 105; lava deposits, 94–5; seeds from, 99; its size, 94 *n*.2

Chloroform, D. and its discovery, 159, 166

Cholsey-cum-Moulsford, H.'s living, 65, 89 and *n*., 90–1

Chonos Archipelago, 98; dried ('potato') plants from, 108 and *n*., 126, 132

Chronometers, 48 and *n*.

Clark, William, birth of a son, 79 and *n*.

Clark, John Willis, biog., 79 *n*.

Clift, William, 77; biog., 83 *n*., 118 *n*.; and the Megatherium specimen, 78, 83, 89, 120

Cocos chewing, 149

Colburn, Henry (*d*. 1855), publisher of D.'s *Narrative*, 134 and *n*.1, 141–2

Conception Island, 76, 100, 242; geology of, 100, 105; nearby volcanoes, 82

Copiapò, 12, 109, 110, 242

Coquimbo, 107, 108

Cordillera, the, *see* Andes

Corfield, R., D. and, 96 *n*.2, 99

Corn Laws, 156

Covington, Syms, servant to D., 75 and *n*.

Cuming, Hugh, biog., 121 *n*.1; and the Galapagos Islands, 121 and *n*.

Cuvier, Leopold (1769–1832), *Anatomie des mollusques*, 67, 69, 92, 94

Darwin, Caroline, and Charles's education, 2

Darwin, Catherine, xii; D.'s letter to, 75 *n*.1

DARWIN, CHARLES

Biographical and personal:
    acquires servant, 75 and *n*.; application for Government grant, 127, 134 and *n*.2; birth of children, 155, 160 and *n*.3, 161, 166; Childhood and schooldays, 1, 2; and classical learning, 161–2, 171; company investment, 168–9; concern over specimens, 117, 118–23; despatches boxes to Cambridge, 123; disposition of collection, 39–40, 42, 46; early friendship with H., 1, 4, 7–8, 9, 14, 15, 221; engagement, 148; on FitzRoy, 28 *n*.2, 37, 39, 40, 41; heavy burden of literary work, 17; ill-health, 15, 17, 52 *n*., 96 and *n*.1, 98, 136, 140, 157, 160–1, 163, 165; increasing fame, 15; influence of

Beagle voyage on character, 8; inland expeditions in S. America, 11–12, 55ff.; longing for home, 63–4, 73–4, 95, 100, 112, 115; marriage to Emma Wedgwood, 3, 14, 15; misery at leaving England, 52 *n*.; moves to Down House, 15; moves to London, 13, 14, 118 and *n*.1, 120; offered post of naturalist in the *Beagle*, 1–3, 9, 19; opinion of Owen, 118 *n*.2; preparations for sailing, 51–2; prepares to join ship, 37ff.; purchases farm in Lincs, 155, 157 and *n*.1; on quarters in the *Beagle*, 46–7, 48–9; reaction to *Beagle* offer, 32–7; relations with brothers and sisters, 2, 13; relations with father, 2–3, 34–5, 49, 70; returns to England, 12, 100, 117–18; sails from England, 10, 47–8, 51, 52; secretaryship of Geological Society, 138–40, 140 *n*.2; and Sedgwick, 9, 56–7; on shipmates, 46, 49, 56; stowing of goods, 43–4, 46; University, 1, 6; on the voyage, 52ff., 91

General scientific:
    cell-making instinct of some hymenoptera, 201 and *n*., 215–16; use of clinometer, 25 and *n*., 41; di- and tri-morphism, 207 and *n*.1, 208; evolutionary theory, 18, 175 *n*.; geological theories at St Jago, 53 and *n*.1; use of Goniometer, 82, 89–90; inheritance of unit characters, 209 *n*.2; use of 'inosculating', 62 and *n*.2; on an instinct for scientific research, 159. Natural Selection, 12, 160 *n*.1, 185 *n*.; notes and collections of seeds for species-forming theories, 175ff.; use of sympiesometer, 39; theories of land-upheaval, 11, 53, 103, 234–5; variations in large and small genera, 175 *n*.; wish to study mathematics, 47, 49, 50

Botany: at Cambridge, 5–7; Darwin's ignorance of, 58, 80, 124; experimental interest in weeds, 81 and *n*., 211; necessity for drying specimens, 89; sea-and water-transport of seeds and plants, 172 and *n*., 176–7, 201, 202; work on grasses, 174

Corallines: first mention of, 53 and *n*.2; D.'s interest in, 72 and *n*.2; from Patagonia, 84; of Tierra del Fuego, 85–6, 93–4; submergence of Diego Garcia and, 130

Entomology: collection of Arachnidae, 58, 97–8; collection of Diptera and Hymenoptera from Chiloe, 101; observations in S. America, 55–6; transport of specimens, 86–7

Fossil mammals: mammoth, 92; mastodon from Port St Julien, 84–5; *Megatherium*,

11, 61, 74, 76, 77, 83–5; Clift and, 78, 83, 84, 89; transport to Cambridge, 88, 89, 97

Geology: catalogue of D.'s specimens, 58 and n.; determination of Chalazite (Chabazine), 147 and n.; H.'s advice on, 65–6, 67; influence on D.'s thought, 10–11; notes from the Beagle, 138–40, 141, 147, 157, and n.2; study of volcanic rocks, 82, 93, 96, 109

Ornithology: existence of two species of ostrich, 86 and n.; observations on, 62 and nn.1, 2, 63, 75, 80

Plants mentioned: Anacharis (Elodea), 173 and n.; Astelia pumila (Anthericum trifarium), 135 and n.1; Berberis, 89 and n.3; Drosera, 211 and n., 212, 215; Eryngium, 133 and n.; Fungi, 132 (Stinkhorn, 42 and n.1); Lychnis, 174, 176; Myzodendron ('parasitical bush'), 131 and n.; Nothofagus, 85 and n., 127, 131 n.; Ranunculus biternatus, 89 and n.2

Seeds: counting of in Geum and Epilobium, etc., 175, 176; immersion in salt water, 176, 195 and n.1; longevity, 153–4, 154 n.; packing and transporting, 232 and n.; sent home from Beagle expedition, 80–1, 84, 87, 92, 97, 99, 107

Zoology: bridge from geology to, 11; Leiodes, 42, 57; Planariae, 58, 59, 92, 97; observations on Cape Verde Islands, 53–4, Monte Video (Zoophites), 63; southern ocean (Crustacea), 72; work on the Cirripedia, 159 and n.3, 160, 162 and n.2, 167, 174, 185

Writings:
Autobiography, 7–8; ill-health, 15–16; misery at leaving England, 52 n.; on Whewell, 87 n.; on Herschel, 116 n.; and Brown, 125 n.; memories of Henslow, 224–6; and the Cirripides, 227
The Balanidae, 162 n.
Cirripedia, 159 and n.3, 160, 162 and n.2, 170–1, 171 n., 227–8
Coral Reefs, 130 n.
Diary of the Voyage of H.M.S. Beagle, 11, 15, 40 n.; and fossil Megatherium, 11, 61; plans for publication, 124–8 passim, 128 n.2, 130–7 passim, 141–2; D.'s collaborators, 134 n.2; the prospectus, 142; completion, 158
The Different Forms of Flowers on Plants of the Same Species, 207 n.1
The Formation of Vegetable Mould, 149 and n.
The Geology of the Voyage of the 'Beagle', 157 and n.2, 158
Insectivorous Plants, 211 n.

Journal of Researches, 14, 40 n.4, 128 n.1; advice to collectors, 230–3
'Little Diaries', 40 n., 91–2, 99
On the Origin of Species . . ., unpublished sketches for, 8; opposition aroused by its publication, 19, 202, 203–4, 205–7, 209–10, 213–14
Ornithology, 62 n.1, 86 n.
The structure and distribution of coral reefs, 234
Zoology of the Voyage of the 'Beagle', 14, 26 n.4, 147; Darwin's collaborators, 134 n.2

Darwin, Dr Erasmus (1731–1802), and Wedgwood, 3
Darwin, Erasmus Alvey (brother of Charles); letter to H., 69, 76–7; life and character, 13–14
Darwin, Henrietta (b. 1843, d. of Charles, later Mrs Litchfield), Emma Darwin, 13 and n.2, 14, 70 and n., 148, 198 and n.1
Darwin, Horace, s. of Charles, 149 n.1
Darwin, Leonard, s. of Charles, 13 n.1
Darwin, Dr Robert (1766–1848), attitude to Charles' appointment to the Beagle, 2, 32–3, 35, 43, 111; character, 2, 70; at Etruria, 3; gives financial support to his family, 14; letters to, 34–5; letters from, 70–1, 111; marriage to Susannah Wedgwood, 1, 3, 4
Darwin, Susan, 97 n.2
Darwin, William Erasmus, s. of Charles, 198 and n.2
Daubeny, Professor Charles Giles Bridle, 194 n.1; biog., 209 n.1
de Beer, Sir Gavin, and D.'s planned visit to S. America, 40 n.4; 9 n.1, 75 n.1, 206 n.1
de Candolle, Alphonse, Géographie Botanique, 191 and n.2
de Perthes, Jacques Boucher, Crèvecoeur, and hand-worked flints, 215 and n.
Diego Garcia, 130 and n.
Don, David, 124 and n., 143
D'Orbigny, Dessalines (1802–57), 133; and species of Eryngium, 133 and n.; geology of the Pampas, 110
Down House, Kent, D. moves to, 15–16; houses Darwin's Geological Catalogue, 58 and n.; its situation, 16; purchase of, 14; the worm-stone, 149 n.1
Draper, Professor, paper to British Academy (1860), 209 n.1
Drummond, J. C., The Englishman's Food, 156 n.
Drummond, Thomas, lime-light, 149 and n.2

Dunning, Dr F. W., and St Peter and St Paul's Rocks, 54 *n*.1

East Indian Archipelago, chewing of Betel, 149
Edinburgh Review, attacks *The Origin of Species*, 118 *n*.2, 204, 206
Edinburgh University, D. and, 1
Etruria, 3
Eiseley, Loren C., and Blyth's influence on Darwin, 62 *n*.2
Eyton, Thomas Campbell, 62 and *n*., 129, 130; opponent of Darwin, 27 *n*.2; writings, 27 *n*.2

Falkland Island, 48, 71; D.'s arrival at, 73; geology of, 73
Fernando Noronha, 48, 54, 126
FitzRoy, Captain Robert, 92 *n*.2; and the *Beagle*, 2, 9, 10, 11, 28; biog., 28 *n*.2; his character, 31; D. joins his ship, 37, 38; letter to *S. African Christian Recorder*, 114 *n*.; plans for publication, 124–5, 128 and *n*.2; purchase of a schooner, 73–4; and repatriated Fuegians, 73 *n*.1; Survey, 60 and *n*.; *Surveying Voyages of Adventure and Beagle*, 39 *n*., 40 *n*.2; use of a sympiesometer, 39 *n*.
Forbes, Edward, biog., 153 *n*.; and Ipswich Museum, 159 *n*.1
Freke, Dr, and *The Origin of Species*, 214 and *n*.2
Freycinet, Louis Claude (1779–1842), *Voyage . . . de 'l'Uranie'*, 129, 130

Galapagos Islands, 109; Cuming and, 121 and *n*.1; D. and their flora, 113 and *nn*.1, 2, 121, 125, 132; dried fish from, 126; geology of, 113–14; influence of D.'s thought, 10, 12; publication of botanical collections from, 129 *n*.
Gamlingay expedition, 127, 129, 222
Gardeners' Chronicle, 154 *n*., 176; Henslow and, 186 and *n*.1
Gay, Claude, and the Cordillera, 96 and *n*.1; and viviparous lizard, 96 *n*.1, 107
Geological Society, D.'s wish to join, 115, 122; the Secretaryship, 138–40
Gilmour, J. S. L., 5 and *n*.
Goniometers, 82, 89–90
Gosse, Philip Henry, and the aquarium, 173 and *n*.2, 174
Gould, John (1804–81), 134 *n*.2
Gray, George Robert (1808–72), 134 *n*.2
Great Exhibition (Paris), 186 *n*.2, 187 *n*.1
Gully, James Manby (1808–83), his cold water cure, 163–4, 165

Halley's Comet, 74; prediction of its return, 78 *n*.1
Harling, Gunnar, D. and the flora of Galapagos Islands, 113 *n*.1
Harris, William Snow, and lightning conductors, 49 and *n*.
Henfrey, Arthur (1819–59), 186 *n*.2
Henslow, Frances, marriage to Joseph Hooker, xi, 21, 160 *n*.1, 164 and *n*.
Henslow, George, his career and views, 193 and *n*.1
HENSLOW, JOHN STEVENS
Life and character:
academic career, 4–5; advice to D. on his character, 50–1, 79; birth of a daughter, 78–9; character and attainments, 18–19, 221ff.; and D.'s engagement, 148–9; and D.'s marriage, 15, 19; D.'s recollections of, 221–6; death of his mother, 191–2; death of his wife, 197 and *n*.; his friendship with D. 4, 6–8, 14, 15–19, 221ff., 224ff.; on his own happiness, 148; involvement in Cambridge politics, 45 and *n*., 65; and the living of Cholsey-cum-Moulsford, 65, 89 and *n*., 90; publishes extracts from D.'s early letters, xi–xii, 107 *n*.2; recommends D. for post of naturalist in the *Beagle*, 1–2, 29–30, 223; Rector of Hitcham, Suffolk, 16–17, 18, 89 *n*.1, 138, 170, 223–6
Scientific topics:
Address in Ipswich Museum, 159 and *n*.1; advice to D. on geology, 65–6, 67; advice to D. on sending specimens, 66–8; and the British Association, 65; contribution to Great Exhibition, 187 *n*.1; and D.'s *Planariae* (Oncidium), 66–7; on hand-worked flints, 214 and *n*.1; Hitcham Flora, 174, 180; influence on natural history, 4–7, 17, 164, 221; his judgement on D.'s views, 205–6; receives D.'s boxes from the *Beagle*, 65, 66–8, 77–8; and Suffolk Crag, 155; use of clinometer, 44–5; work on insect and fungi damage, 195 and *n*.2
Herbert, John Maurice, 56 and *n*.
Herschel, Sir John, biog., 116 *n*.1; D. and, 116 and *n*.1
Hobart, 113, 243
Hooker, Sir Joseph Dalton, biog., 160 *n*.1; and D's botanical collections, 129 *n*.; Director of Kew Gardens, 21, 160 *n*.1; *Essay on the Tasmanian Flora*, 186 *n*.2; friendship with D., 18; H.'s letter to on D.'s hypothesis, 205–6; influence on static view of species, 186 *n*.2; *Introductory Essay to the Flora Indica*, 186 *n*.2; letters from, 165, 167, 168; marriage to

Frances Henslow, xi, 21, 160 *n.*1, 164 and *n.*; at the Paris Exhibition, 187 *n.*1; 'Plants of the Galapagos Islands', 121 *n.*1; publications, 160 *n.*1, 186 and *n.*2

Hooker, Sir William J., 78, 95 *n.*, 153, 177 *n.*; Director of Kew Gardens, xi, 5, 160 *n.*1; friendship with D. and H., xi

Hope, Frederick William, biog., 121 and *n.*2

Humboldt, Friedrich Baron von (1769–1859), *Aspects of Nature*, 26 *n.*3; *Personal Narrative*, 2, 26; on Brown, 125 *n.*1; D.'s admiration for, 53, 55, 57; and the Dragon Tree, 26 *n.*3; letter to D., 26 *n.*2

Huxley, Thomas Henry (1825–95), 209 *n.*1; and parthenogenesis, 209 *n.*2

Indian Archipelago, 28, 31

Indian Ocean, specimens from, 149; submergence of Diego Garcia, 130 and *n.*

Indians, war of extermination against, 81

Innes, Rev. Brodie, Vicar of Down, 167 *n.*1, 168, 190 and *n.*

Ipswich Museum, 159 *n.*1; *Cirripedia* specimens, 170

Ipswich Society, 159 *n.*1, 171

Iquique, 110

Isle of France, 113

Isle of Wight, 142

Jenyns, Leonard, 125 *n.*3, 135; and the *Beagle*, 28, 48–9, 50; D. and, 221; D.'s collaborator in *Fish*, 134 *n.*2, 141 and D.'s Planariae, 66; at Ely, 78; and the Galapagos fish, 126, 132; ill-health, 158; *Memoir of . . . H.*, 26, 45 *n.*, 159 *n.*1, 170 *n.*, 195 *n.*2; present of Diptera to D., 26–7

Keeling Islands, 132, 149

Kemp, W., his Atriplex plant, 151–4

Kerguelen Island, Hooker's plants from, 172

Keynes, Margaret, 13 *n.*1

King, Capt. (later Rear-Admiral) Peter Parker, expedition to S. America, 28 *n.*2, 31 *n.*1, 40 and *n.*2, 41, 73 *n.*1; his Journal, 124

King George's Sound, 113

Kingsley, Charles (1819–75), and D.'s theories, 213 *nn.*1, 2

Kirby, Rev. W., and Ipswich Museum, 159 *n.*1

Lake Argentino, 92 *n.*2

Lamarck, Jean Baptiste (1744–1829), 94

Leighton, Rev. W. A., *Flora of Shropshire*, 226

Levaillant, François (1743–1824), *Travels*, 4, 117 and *n.*

Lindley, John, 192; biog., 151 *n.*

Lima, 101, 109, 242

Linnaeus, Carl (1707–78), 94

Linnean Society, 40 *n.*1, 122 and *n.*3, 123, 135; Duke of Somerset as President, 127; *Journal*, 195 and *n.*

Litchfield, Mrs H. E., *see* Darwin, Henrietta

London Catalogue of Plants, 174, 175, 178

London University, 128; early history, 125 and *n.*2

Lonsdale, William, 122 and *n.*4; kindness to D., 122

Lowe, Richard Thomas, 42 and *n.*3, 50, 67

Lumb, Edward, 80; letter to Henslow, 88

Lyell, Sir Charles, 14; and D.'s specimens, 118, 119–20, 122, 128; his find of handworked flints, 214 and *n.*; and plant dispersal by means of icebergs, 172 *n.*; *Principles of Geology*, 10–11, 53 and *n.*1, 110; *Travels*, 155

Maclear, Sir Thomas, 116 and *n.*2

Macleay, William Sharp, quinary system of classification, 62 and *n.*2

Maer, family home of Wedgwoods, 3, 9, 13, 34

Maldive Is., 149

Malthus, Thomas Robert (1766–1834), *Essay on Population*, 185 and *n.*

Martyn, Thomas (1735–1825), Prof. of Botany, 4, 5

Mendel, Gregor Johann (1822–84), and inheritance of unit characters, 209 *n.*2

Mendoza, 12, 102, 107; seeds from, 108

Miller, William Hallowes, and D.'s specimens, 126 and *n.*3, 141, 147

Milton, John, D. and, 63 and *n.*

Monte Video, 48, 54; D. at, 57ff., 84; geology of, 57; ornithological observations, 62 and *n.*2

Murray, John (1808–92), publisher of *Origin of Species*, 202 and *n.*

Narborough, Sir John (1640–88), 94

New South Wales, D.'s dislike of, 113

New Zealand, 114; death of 'Comte Thierry', 154–5

Owen, Sir Richard, 27 *n.*2, 83 *n.*, 209 *n.*1; attacks *The Origin of Species*, 118 *n.*, 202 and *n.*, 203–4, 206; biog., 118 *n.*2; D.'s collaborator in *Fossil Mammalia*, 134 *n.*; and D.'s specimens, 118–19; *Lectures on the Invertebrae*, 210; and parthenogenesis, 209 *n.*2

Pacific Ocean, 76, 114
Parana River, 82
Pampas, geology of, 110; 'Giant thistle' ('Cardoon'), 126 and *n*.2, 133
Patagonia, 11, 31 and *n*.2, 47, 48; D. and the coast, 60–1; geological interests, 76, 105, 106; the great Southern formation, 84; plants from, 84, 97
Peacock, Rev. George, 147; and the appointment of the *Beagle*, 28, 30; biog., 28 *n*.1, his inaccuracy, 31 and *nn*., 40 and *n*.4; letters from, 28–9, 31–2
Peru, revolution in, 108, 110
Plinian Society of Edinburgh, D. and, 1
Port Alegra, 80–1
Port Desire, 84, 133, 242
Port Famine, 85
Port St Julian, 84, 242
Poole, John, *Paul Pry*, 40 and *n*.3
Potato disease, 156 and *n*.
Punta Alta, 11
Powell, Rev. Baden, and D.'s theories, 206 and *n*.

Ramsay, Marmaduke, and Canary Islands, 9, 26 and *n*.; his death, 29, 33, 52; memorial Jesus Chapel, 78, 87
Ransome family, 166 and *n*.1, 199
Raspe, Rudolf Erich (1737–94), *Baron von Münchausen*, 59 and *n*.
Ray Society, 147, 152 *n*., 162 *n*.2, 170–1
Rio de Janeiro, 48; D. at, 52–7; entomological collection, 58–9; inland expedition to Rio Macaò, 55
Rio de la Plata, 57, 59, 83, 102; its country, 61; D. at Maldonado, 74–5
Rio Maypo, 96
Rio Negro, 60, 61, 71, 74
Rio Santa Cruz, 92; geology of the valley, 93
Royal Geographical Society, 14, 92 *n*.2
Royal Society, 122 *n*.3; Sabine's Presidential Address, 165 *n*.
Royal Zoological Society, 16
Royle, John Forbes (1799–1858), 139

Sabine, General Sir Edward, biog., 165 and *n*.
St Fé, 81–2
St Helena, 115–17, 243
St Jago, 53, 56, 58
Sandwith, N. H., notes by, 85, 95, 96, 113, 121, 126, 131, 133, 135
Santa Cruz, 53, 242
Sedgwick, Professor Adam, 2, 40, 66, 68, 74, 76; and the Brit. Ass., 77 and *n*.; to leave Cambridge, 120; and Cambridge Philosophical Society, 4; and D. at

Cambridge, 9, 10: and the Geological Society, 115; opponent of D., 4, 25 *n*., 204, 205, 206; Welsh geological tour, 25 *n*., 33, 56–7
Shrewsbury, 1, 2, 3, 13, 117
Shrewsbury School, 1
Sierra de la Ventana, D.'s ascent of, 81
Smith, Dr S., ix, x, 12 *n*.1
Smith, Dr A., biog., 116 and *n*.3, 117
Solander, Daniel Charles (1736–82), 135
South African Christian Recorder, letter from D. and FitzRoy, 114 *n*.
South Sea Islands, 28, 31, 85
Spring Rice, Thomas, Baron Monteagle, 45 *n*.; and D.'s application for a govt. grant, 134 and *n*.2, 136, 138, 143
Stecher, R. M., and D.-Innes Letters, 167 *n*.
Stoddart, D. R., ix, 130 *n*., 234
Straits of Magellan, 76, 82, 93, 242; their desolate landscape, 94
Sympiesometer, 39; definition of, 39 *n*.2
Sydney, price of land in, 112

Tahiti, 114, 243
Talcuana Island, 100
Teneriffe, 53; its great Dragon Tree, 26 and *n*.3
Tierra del Fuego, 48, 76, 241; D. on the natives, 71–2, 73; a final adieu, 98; its geology, etc., 72, 84–5; presentation of articles from, 151; repatriation of Fuegians, 73 and *n*.1; second visit to, 82; shipment of plants from, 84; suggested survey of, 28, 29–30, 31
Tollet, Mr, 191 and *n*.1
Turner, William Dawson (1775–1858), xi, 21

Uruguay, the, 82

Valparaiso, 11–12, 75, 242; D. at, 95ff.; earthquake in, 100

Wallace, Alfred Russel (1823–1913), 27 *n*.2; and Natural Selection, 160 *n*.1, 175 *n*., 228
Waterhouse, George R. (1810–88), 134 *n*.2
Watson, Hewett Cottrell, biog., 180 *n*.
Way, Albert (1805–74), 27 and *n*.1; *Promptorium Parvulorum*, 27 *n*.
Wedgwood, Emma, marriage to Darwin, 3, 14, 15
Wedgwood, Josiah (1730–95), of Etruria, 3
Wedgwood, Josiah, s. of above, 1, 15; and D.'s joining the *Beagle*, 3, 34, 35–7; letters from, 35–7

Wedgwood, Julia, 14
Wedgwood, Sara, 211 *n.*
Wedgwood, Susannah, marriage to Robert
 Darwin, 1, 3
Weissmann, August (1834–1914), George
 Henslow and, 193 *n.*
Werner, *Nomenclature of Colours*, 82
 and *n.*
Westwood, John Obadiah, 122 and *n.*1
Whewell, Rev. William, 127; his influence
 on D., 87 and *n.*, 140; work on tides

(*History of the Inductive Sciences*), 87
 and *n.*, 159
William IV, Coronation, 10
Willis, Robert, 79 and *n.*

Yarrell, William, 40, 122; biog., 40 *n.*1

Zoological Museum, its unnamed specimens, 119 and *n.*1
Zoological Society, 50 *n.*1; its quarrelsome
 spirit, 121